THE · BUSINESS · SIDE · OF · GENERAL · PRACTICE

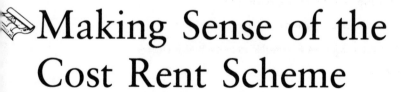

Making Sense of the Cost Rent Scheme

EDITED BY
JOHN CHISHOLM

WITH A FOREWORD BY
MICHAEL WILSON

RADCLIFFE MEDICAL PRESS
OXFORD

© 1992 Radcliffe Medical Press Ltd
15 Kings Meadow, Ferry Hinksey Road, Oxford OX2 0DP

British Library Cataloguing in Publication Data

A catalogue record for this book is available from the British Library

ISBN 1-870905-56-3

Typeset by Advance Typesetting Ltd, Oxfordshire
Printed and bound in Great Britain by TJ Press Ltd, Padstow, Cornwall

Contents

Making Sense of the Cost Rent Scheme

Contributors

JOHN CHISHOLM, *Joint Deputy Chairman and Negotiator, General Medical Services Committee, British Medical Association*

COLIN FOOT, *General Manager, Shropshire Family Health Services Authority*

RAY MORGAN, *formerly General Manager, General Practice Finance Corporation*

RUSSELL WALSHAW, *Chairman, Practice Premises Subcommittee, General Medical Services Committee, British Medical Association*

PAUL WHITTLESTONE, *Director, Rawlinson, Kelly & Whittlestone Ltd*

MICHAEL WILKS, *General Practitioner, East Sheen*

Editor

JOHN CHISHOLM, *Joint Deputy Chairman and Negotiator, General Medical Services Committee, British Medical Association*

The Business Side of General Practice

Editorial Board

Foreword

THE cost rent scheme has undoubtedly been the catalyst in stimulating the dramatic improvement in general practice premises over the last 20 years. It has encouraged general practitioners to invest capital in their practice premises by providing a return sufficient to service their capital investment. This has transformed general practice in many parts of the country, particularly in those areas where suitable sites have been available for development. The challenge for the next 20 years is in continuing that process, and extending it into areas where new sites are not available, where difficulties abound and where imaginative solutions are required.

This book is essential reading for anyone involved in premises development for the cost rent scheme is complex. Necessarily complex perhaps, for the original relatively simple scheme for the building of new surgeries has been extended to cover imaginative solutions, such as conversions, major improvements, landlord schemes, etc.

The imposition of cash limits in 1990 on the funds available for cost rents could prove to be either a brake or a spur to premises development. It will certainly be a brake if allocations are inadequate, but the necessity to bid for funds could mean better forward planning by practices, a spur to Family Health Services Authorities to facilitate that forward planning and provide practices with the encouragement to develop their premises to meet patients needs. This book makes a major contribution to that process.

MICHAEL WILSON
May 1992

Preface

GOOD premises make an immense contribution to the effectiveness of primary health care, whereas cramped or sub-standard premises in poor condition inevitably affect patients and general practitioners and their staff adversely. The development of better premises therefore has many potential benefits: more congenial and pleasant surroundings for all those who use them; the opportunity to provide a wider range of services; the scope for more effective teamwork; and, it is to be hoped, the possibility of improved patient care.

Purchasing, building or developing surgery premises is the most significant financial commitment of a general practitioner's (GP's) professional career. That burden has been eased significantly by the Cost Rent Scheme, introduced in the 1970s, which has played a major part in the widespread modernization of surgery premises which has occurred in recent years. The Cost Rent Scheme provides financial support for the building of new premises, for the acquisition of premises for conversion, and for the improvement of existing surgery accommodation, and aims to cover the interest charged on a loan financing an acceptable project.

One new uncertainty that GPs have had to confront since radical contractual changes were imposed on the profession on 1 April 1990 has been the responsibility of Family Health Services Authorities (FHSAs) and Health Boards to manage cash limits covering many elements of direct reimbursement, including the funding of cost rent schemes and improvement grant schemes. GPs now have to face the prospect that funds will not be available when required for the scheme proposed for their own practice, and undoubtedly some GPs and their patients will have been disadvantaged by the new rules. The overall picture is not yet clear, but there is some encouraging anecdotal evidence that applications for loans for premises development are remaining buoyant.

The provisions of the Cost Rent Scheme are specified in paragraph 51 of the Statement of Fees and Allowances Payable to General Medical Practitioners – the SFA or Red Book – and any practice embarking on a cost rent project, or even contemplating that possibility, needs to understand those provisions. Only the original text carries the force of law and provides the detail needed for authoritative interpretation and for the resolution of any dispute as to meaning. However, the style of the Red Book is complex, daunting and densely legalistic – indeed, perhaps nowhere more so than in the 12 pages explaining the Rent and Rates Scheme and the further 46 containing all the details of the Cost Rent Scheme.

This book has a different purpose: not only to be an essential adjunct to the Red Book, explaining its provisions in simpler terms where possible, but also to give practical insights into the design and financing of premises.

The six authors contribute to that purpose from their different perspectives, looking at the development of practice premises from the standpoints of a GP, an architect, an FHSA general manager and a financier. Inevitably, there is some overlap between the contributions, but that repetition has been retained in order to preserve valuable individual insights from the differing viewpoints of the authors.

Michael Wilks has written the first chapter, a general practitioner's view of the need for premises. The second section of the book has been contributed by Paul Whittlestone and the third by Ray Morgan, giving advice based on vast experience on the designing and construction of premises and on their financing. Colin Foot in writing the fourth part of the book guides the reader through the complexities of the SFA, covering not only the Cost Rent Scheme but also the Improvement Grant Scheme and the Rent and Rates Scheme, while Russell Walshaw has contributed the part of chapter 16 dealing with self-supply and VAT registration. The first two chapters of the final section of the book have also been written by Colin Foot, and I have written the last three chapters on partnership agreements, taxation, and avoiding the pitfalls.

The Business Side of General Practice

The present volume is the sixth in a series of books entitled *The Business Side of General Practice*, which has developed from an original idea proposed by Stuart Carne. It is envisaged that potential readers of such books will not only include GPs, but also trainee practitioners, doctors' professional advisers and their ancillary staff, particularly practice managers, receptionists and all those involved in the administration of the doctor's office. Clearly this volume will have particular value for doctors' professional advisers, practice managers and vocational trainees, as well as being essential reading for any GP embarking on the development of premises.

With such a readership in mind, an Editorial Board for *The Business Side of General Practice* was formed. It deliberately includes representatives of both the elected members and the secretariat of the General Medical Services Committee of the British Medical Association; a representative of the Royal College of General Practitioners; a Local Medical Committee secretary; a Family Health Services Authority general manager; and representatives of the Association of Health Centre and Practice Administrators and of the Association of Medical Secretaries, Practice Administrators and Receptionists. As a result, experts on terms and conditions of service, on training and education, and on the needs of readers, have been brought together to share their experience.

Acknowledgements

I am most grateful to all my fellow authors for their hard work and for the quality of their contributions to this project, and to the Editorial Board for their helpful comments on the initial drafts of the text. Russell Walshaw and Emma Douglas were co-opted onto the Board for this book, and their expertise has proved particularly valuable.

I also wish to thank Valerie Martin of Touche Ross and Mike Hamilton of the Primary Care and Community Unit, Lothian Health Board for their comments on the text; Rawlinson, Kelly and Whittlestone Ltd. for the illustrations; and Tony Stanton, my fellow Joint Deputy Chairman of the General Medical Services Committee, Trevor Baldry of Grant Thornton and John Dean of Pannell Kerr Forster for their valued advice. The whole project has been greatly aided by financial support from TSB Bank plc.

Michael Wilson, Norman Ellis and Bill Kent have given me considerable personal encouragement concerning *The Business Side of General Practice* series, and Norman Ellis has been a staunch ally in the task of sub-editing the manuscripts. I am particularly pleased that Michael Wilson, the immediate past Chairman of the General Medical Services Committee, has agreed to contribute the foreword to this book – I suspect that no other GP in the country has greater practical personal experience of cost rent schemes.

Finally, I must thank Andrew Bax for his cheerful and energetic enthusiasm, his generosity of spirit and his practical advice throughout the lengthy preparation of this book. Its period of gestation has far exceeded not only that of any mammal known to science, but all the more optimistic predictions of those involved with the project. It has I believe been worth waiting for – I hope it will prove a valuable and helpful guide for all those with an interest in promoting and producing high standard general practice premises.

JOHN CHISHOLM
April 1992

Section 1

1 The Need for Premises

THE majority of general practitioners practise from premises in which they have some kind of financial stake. They either rent or – usually via substantial loans – own their practice accommodation. If they rent, the practice receives reimbursement based on an assessment of the property's value on the open rental market. If they are owner-occupiers, then the same assessment may apply, but the more adventurous, who want to develop their premises, will aim for a more complex, but ultimately more satisfactory, basis for reimbursement – the cost rent.

The Cost Rent Scheme is what this book is about. The details, pitfalls and procedures deserve careful study, for careful study will not only be, literally, repaid, but will also help doctors to avoid costly mistakes or end up with the one thing they may resent for as long as they use the building – compromise.

It is important to say at the outset that the Cost Rent Scheme is not for the faint-hearted. Neither can corners be cut or a scheme devised without a considerable outlay of time: time for planning, partnership discussions, meetings with the practice accountant, architects, builders, banks and Family Health Services Authority (FHSA) or Health Board. All the effort put into proper planning will be worth it. Many practices, perhaps all, underestimate the need to give time. It is important as part of the very first steps to identify one member of the practice – not necessarily a partner – who will oversee the project, and to give adequate time to that individual so that a proper job is done.

Before the publication of this book, there was only one way to prepare yourself for doing battle with the intricacies of cost rent; that was to read the Red Book, otherwise known as the Statement of Fees and Allowances. The sections in the Red Book on reimbursement of premises are sometimes difficult to follow, but cannot be ignored. It is hoped that this book will place the Red Book paragraphs in context, and also to explain the order in which the various steps should normally be taken.

It is important, also, to look at the effect the new contractual arrangements for GPs, introduced on 1 April 1990, have made on the planning of cost rent projects, particularly because of the introduction of cash limits. In what seems to be a time of constant change in the NHS, many GPs will be uncertain about the size and scope of the alterations they will wish to make to their work, what services they wish to provide, and also therefore the effect an uncertain future will have on the design of premises.

What is clear, however, is that the new financial climate, the streamlining of the administration of FHSAs and Health Boards, and the new budgetary relationship between Regions and FHSAs, will all increase the pressure on individual practices not only to plan effectively for the future, but to appreciate the need to look at their plans in a competitive light. In the same way that the FHSA or Health Board has discretion to vary the rate of reimbursement on a variable allocation of practice staff, so it also has a greater freedom than hitherto to stray outside the current tight definitions of acceptable practice design into a freer interpretation of what is good or bad, and what in its view is acceptable and reimbursable. The future is uncertain, but we would hope that the enthusiastic practice, prepared to exploit the contract and prepared to put work into reflecting its commitment in the design and operation of its premises, will be successful.

So, if you are a doctor intent on developing your premises, and you are determined to proceed, you need to ask yourself two questions:

- Why change?
- Why cost rent?

Why change?

Clearly the answers to this question will be as numerous as the number of practices in the country, but the reasons given will almost always include a lack of space in current premises, a desire to expand and a wish to provide more services. The method of reimbursement on a practice's existing premises (probably a notional rent) may well be an incentive to change, in that it may be inadequately reimbursing outlay, but the primary motivation for change should not be financial. The first consideration must be to take a realistic look at what is wrong with the current premises, and in what way you would wish to see changes made within your overall future plans for the practice. Your needs may be met without moving through substantial modification of your existing premises.

Why cost rent?

Simply because it has the potential for combining maximum financial return with maximum flexibility. In theory, the perfectly arranged cost rent will repay the doctors' interest element on their loan, including an allowance for professional fees. With the historic movement of property values it also has in the past had the potential to repay, over the period of a loan taken out to finance the project, a proportion of the capital outlay, given the option doctors have had to choose more advantageous methods of reimbursement at various stages. As far as flexibility is concerned, the opportunity exists to provide, within the confines of the scheme, a wide variety of accommodation adaptable to such needs as teaching, screening, special clinics and, most importantly, future expansion.

It is probably a mistake to view the project as one that will make money for the doctors involved. There are too many uncertainties in the property market for doctors to feel confident that profits are inevitable. It is also worth remembering that the more specialized the building – and it is clearly desirable for premises to reflect as closely as possible the design ideals of the practice – the more limited its value on the open market. In other words, a cost rent project in an urban area that involves the modification of an existing house may have greater potential for resale to a wider group of potential purchasers than a highly specialized clinic, which can only be sold on to the successors of the partners who built it, or to other doctors. The former will, however, be full of compromises; the latter should provide the ideal working environment for good patient care.

At this stage it is also important to note those areas of expenditure that the Cost Rent Scheme does not cover. These include costs of the initial 'feasibility study' – if it is concluded that the project should not proceed – interest payments which are incurred in excess of the prescribed limits or percentages, maintenance and equipment. Some items which would normally be defined as equipment may be included.

Getting started

Start with a blank sheet of paper and an open mind. The first step is to construct two lists:

1 What is wrong with our present premises?
2 What do we want next time?

See if you can get as many people in the practice as possible to make their own lists. Do not think doctors know it all. Very few GPs would make good receptionists, and asking the opinions of patients and several members of the team is a good way of researching the project well, and producing a feeling of joint involvement from the start.

From this there will emerge a list of priorities which must be discussed at length among the doctors, because they, after all, are the ones who are paying. This meeting will also need to address a number of issues, including the following:

- *Who will take overall charge of the project?* An individual, who may be a doctor, practice manager, or other professional, needs to be identified.
- *What are the likely changes to the practice?* Here the future plans for the practice under the 1990 contract, additional services and clinics, staffing levels, computerization, teaching, library and common room facilities, must be identified. In any plans, additional room for expansion should be built in, if this can be incorporated within the schedules provided in the Red Book (para 51 Schedule 1). It will also be helpful to try and project likely future list sizes from a knowledge of new housing developments, likely practice vacancies locally, and population trends.
- *Are all partners committed to the project?* This is not a necessary prerequisite for success, but what will wreck a project will be a realization half way through that the costs are not going to be equally met. It is vital to know who is in, and who is out, who will be borrowing the money, and that those who are not financially involved can still have a say in all aspects other than financial. It would clearly be ideal for a senior partner close to retirement to be flexible in the face of enthusiasm from his younger colleagues. All such issues can be resolved if discussed fully.
- *What are the likely sources of finance?* Here the partners may wish to explore their own contacts, but a meeting with the practice's clearing bank will be an early priority, once outline plans for the project have emerged. An early meeting with the practice accountant is also essential.
- *Contact with the FHSA or Health Board.* It cannot be emphasized too strongly that the authority must be involved from the outset. With an increase in the power and flexibility of FHSAs – albeit within a tighter Regional control – and of Health Boards, it will be crucial to

the success of a project that the authority is supportive from the outset. Practices have entered, and continue to enter into financial commitments, property purchase, even building, without FHSA or Health Board knowledge and approval. They deserve what they get! It is helpful to have an early meeting with an individual within the authority who can then be identified as a regular point of contact. The FHSA or Health Board will wish to take a view on the need for new premises based on its knowledge of the existing premises, what is available locally, and the overall plans for the growth of the practice.

- *How should an architect be chosen?* There may well be an obvious choice, but remember the essential requirement is for the practice to be quite clear about what it wants, and to be able to brief an architect fully. The architect can only reflect the wishes of the practice in the design if he or she starts with a clear, unequivocal understanding of the essential facts, including the function of rooms, flow of people, position of spaces for different uses in relation to each other, and times and lengths of time different spaces are used. Look at other surgery designs and read the frequent articles in journals about good designs. They have dealt with the kind of problems you are about to face. Use the experience of others.
- *A working knowledge of the Red Book.* This should be gained by at least one of the partners.

Summary

In summary, therefore, try not to run before you have learnt to walk. Feel confident that you have mastered the basic sequence of events. Learn the distinction between the different stages at which interim and final cost rent figures for your reimbursement are established. Spend time away from the immediate pressures of patient care to plan and discuss. Give your architect, bank manager and accountant all the information they need. Involve the FHSA or Health Board. Constantly review progress against the steps we outline in this book. Be prepared to compromise, but start with an ideal.

Please read the whole of this book. In the next chapters we deal with the options to be considered, the pitfalls ahead, and then with detailed outlines of design, finance and reimbursement, to help you make a step by step approach to the final estimation of cost rent. Good luck!

Section 2

Section 2

2 The Choice of Options

A practice may decide to embark upon a cost rent project for a variety of reasons. In most cases, the existing premises will be either too small or unsuitable for the modern medical practice with its emphasis on the fully integrated and multi-professional primary health care team. Many practices are literally bursting at the seams before deciding to search for a solution.

Other doctors may have more of an eye for the future. In today's economic and political climate, and in spite of the uncertainties surrounding the NHS, many family doctors are aware of the need to anticipate future patterns of health care. Well before the year 2000 the ability of a practice to deliver a wide range of primary care services will be of financial, as well as medical and social, concern to the GP. For many practices their ability to deliver such services will be constrained by the premises from which they work. New premises cannot be 'turned on' overnight, and it can take years from 'deciding to do something about it' to celebrating the opening of new or refurbished premises. A wise practice anticipates and plans for the future.

Whether a practice is seeking to solve today's problem or anticipating tomorrow's, the final decision to embark upon a cost rent scheme can only be made once a suitable solution is identified. Since a practice will probably have to live with the outcome of this decision for several decades, it is important that the doctors fully investigate all reasonable alternatives before endorsing a particular strategy. This book will not find the solution to an individual practice's problems, but it will help to provide a framework within which options can be identified and evaluated before a decision is made.

In many cases the time within which critical decisions have to be made may be tight. For instance, the vendor of a well-located property apparently ideal for conversion may be tempted by a more lucrative offer from elsewhere. However, such pressure should not blind doctors to the financial and operational implications of pursuing an unsuitable strategy. It may be unpopular to question the 'perfect' solution, so eloquently advocated by a colleague, but for most doctors there is only one opportunity in their professional lives to make a decision of this magnitude. They owe it to both their practice and their patients to make the right decision. At best a poor decision will represent a lost opportunity, at worst it could severely constrain the future development of the practice.

It is all very well saying that all feasible options should be considered, but what constitutes an option and against what criteria should it be judged?

Experience shows the value of keeping an open mind on options for as long as possible. Favoured options have a habit of falling through. They may also appear good until they are critically appraised against all the practice's requirements, when a less glamorous option which appeared second best on many counts may actually offer a more rational solution. In some cases long-term benefits have to be weighed against short-term costs and disadvantages, while in others the benefits may be short-term but the disadvantages permanent. Balancing the quality of the long-term solution against short-term costs and disruption is a decision which all practices have to face at some stage. Each practice will reach its own decision, but unless the process of making the decision is conducted in an open and rational manner, there is a distinct danger of achieving the worst of all worlds: great expenditure of money and effort, short-term disruption, followed by a growing realization that all this has not achieved the long-term operational benefits envisaged.

Despite the good intentions of the Cost Rent Scheme, there is no quality guarantee attached to the building as a product. Quality can only be achieved by keeping an open mind and making sound decisions throughout a long and complicated process.

To reiterate, there are obvious advantages in considering as many options as possible, even though time may be tight and some solutions may appear unattractive.

Framework for assessment

What is needed is a tool for making quick and accurate assessments of options without expenditure on fees or loss of time. At this stage it is clearly impossible to investigate the detailed design possibilities of each option. Most likely, the practice will not have had the opportunity to develop a detailed brief based both on current needs and aspirations for the future. Indeed, many aspects of the detailed brief are best developed in parallel with the design, so that the interaction of the practice's operational needs and space-planning decisions can be fully appreciated and each used to inform the other. The need at this stage is for a broad framework within which the simple but crucial decison as to whether to reject or pursue an option can be made.

1 Is the proposed site a suitable location with good access for both staff and patients? The practice should be able to form a judgement on this issue.
2 Is the site and building sufficiently large and unconstrained to accommodate the likely (but as yet only loosely defined) practice needs? This applies both to sites for 'new build' solutions and to existing buildings being considered for refurbishment. The potential need for on-site car parking should also be considered. At this point the cost rent area allowances set out in the Red Book provide a reasonable guide to the space requirements of the practice. Some FHSAs and Health Boards are prepared to offer preliminary advice on the suitability of sites and buildings for general medical practice. When considering tightly constrained sites or complicated conversion and refurbishment projects it is always advisable to seek professional design advice at the feasibility stage.
3 Are there likely to be town planning problems? A visit to the local planning department is advised; although it may be necessary to apply and wait for formal approval, the officer should be able to warn of any obvious problems as well as offer any advice on policy and standards (e.g. car parking).
4 Will the option be possible without excessive disruption?
5 Do the sums add up? For most doctors this is the most important issue. It is necessary to develop an estimate of the likely costs of the option for comparison with the project budget. This should anticipate all likely costs, including purchase and building costs, fees and expenses, furnishings, fittings and equipment (although not all these are cost rent allowable). At this stage a budget estimate based upon costs per square metre will suffice. It is always advisable to seek a professional opinion when estimating building costs.

The Red Book states the need to involve the FHSA or Health Board at an early stage. This advice cannot be overemphasized and it is vital to establish contact as soon as a cost rent scheme is being considered and to maintain this contact throughout the whole process. At the very least this will ensure that the practice complies with all the administrative procedures necessary to secure approval and funding under the Cost

Rent Scheme. In addition, FHSAs and Health Boards possess a wealth of knowledge and experience which could prove invaluable to the practice. However, they do vary widely in their approach and in the resources they are able to make available; this clearly affects the time and type of advice they are able to offer.

Unfortunately, because their primary role might be seen as the approval of funding and the administration of the financial aspects of the scheme, some authorities tend to concentrate on compliance with a check list of criteria rather than on taking an overall view of the quality of the proposals. This can make it especially difficult to advise on some of the more intangible, but nevertheless vitally important, design issues, such as the potential of a design to cope with changes in patterns of organization and delivery of primary care services in an uncertain future.

On a more positive note, an increasing number of FHSAs and Health Boards now recognize the value of considering such issues at an early stage in the development of the brief, and actively encourage doctors to prepare a detailed brief as soon as possible.

However, whatever help the FHSA or Health Board is able to give, it is the practice which must shoulder the responsibility for the decisions made. It is also the practice which will pay the price or reap the benefit of the quality of those decisions. This responsibility should be recognized first in the process of developing a comprehensive brief, secondly in selecting the design professionals who will help develop and refine this brief and turn it into a set of design proposals, and thirdly in critically but constructively appraising the quality of these proposals against the brief.

Types of option under the Cost Rent Scheme

There are basically three types of option available to a practice under the Cost Rent Scheme. Their advantages, disadvantages and potential pitfalls are discussed below.

- New purpose-built premises.
- Refurbishment and/or extension of existing practice premises.
- Conversion and/or extension of other premises.

In the latter two cases the solution produced should be of a similar quality to new purpose-built premises.

New purpose-built premises

The prime advantage of new purpose-built premises is that on all but tight sites the design solution should be relatively unconstrained. They also avoid disruption to the day-to-day work of the practice during building works.

However, suitable sites for new building within a practice's existing catchment area may be extremely difficult to find. Sites which are available may command a commercial price higher than the District Valuer is prepared to agree, or may require exceptional works to allow development (e.g. piled foundations), although the cost of such works is potentially allowable as an extra within the Cost Rent Scheme. In some cases planning approvals can present problems where land is designated for another use, or parking or access are difficult.

Refurbishment and/or extension of existing practice premises

The prime advantage of refurbishing or extending existing practice premises is that no alteration to the location of the practice is involved. Moreover, unless the proposal requires the use of an adjoining property, there are none of the problems and delays associated with land and property purchase. In respect of planning, there are no problems of change of use, although any significant works (or any works to listed buildings) will require planning approval. This allows the local authority to impose conditions on its approval, for example more stringent parking requirements. The need for consent should be checked at an early stage.

Inevitably, building work involving the existing practice premises will be disruptive, even if it is phased to minimize such disruption. If necessary, the FHSA or Health Board is able to help with the cost of temporary accommodation.

Conversion and/or extension of other premises

While this may not seem as good a solution as building new premises, it may in practice be the only type of option available. Converting existing accommodaton on several floors may present problems of access for the disabled and emergency exits in case of fire. It is unlikely that the functional equivalent of new purpose-built accommodation can ever be achieved, but good design should avoid too many compromises.

Planning consents can present major problems and should be checked at an early stage.

3 Sketch Plans and Interim Cost Rent Application

Interim cost rent approval

ONCE an option has been identified as both being suitable and representing the best choice available, the next step is to obtain formal approval from the FHSA or Health Board. This is done by making an application for interim cost rent approval. In design terms this involves an architect preparing sketch proposals (usually at 1:100 or 1:50 scale), which should be accompanied by a schedule of accommodation and, where possible, an outline of the costs involved. Authorities, however, vary on this requirement.

The Red Book sets out the maximum area of building upon which a cost rent can be approved, although a practice can always build larger premises if it is prepared to fund the difference. In fact the overall allowable areas are reasonably generous and should present no serious constraint, especially in new premises. It is worth pointing out that buildings more than 5% smaller than the maximum allowances may be subject to a pro rata reduction in cost rent.

The Red Book also sets out a series of recommendations for both minimum and suitable sizes for certain individual rooms. The interpretation of these varies widely from authority to authority; some regard all the minima and recommendations as the mandatory size, while others refuse to sanction spaces not specifically included in the schedule (even though much of the Red Book was written over two decades ago and does not reflect all aspects of current practice). Fortunately some FHSAs and Health Boards are prepared to judge each submission on its merits.

Once the scheme has been submitted, the medical planning and compliance with the recommendations of the Red Book will be assessed. Often the FHSA or Health Board will request a meeting with the practice in their existing premises. The meeting is usually informal and seeks to ascertain whether the design proposals really meet the practice's needs and aspirations. It may be that the scheme will be approved as submitted; more frequently modifications are requested before approval is given; however, if the proposals are considered totally inappropriate, the GPs and architect may be sent back to the drawing board!

Once the authority has approved the scheme, an interim cost rent can be calculated, and if all is well the scheme can proceed to the next stage.

Sketch design proposals

The award of an interim cost rent is the first point at which formal approval of finance is given by the FHSA or Health Board. Since all fees and expenses incurred on abortive work are the responsibility of the practice, it is quite understandable that GPs usually wish to reach this stage rapidly and with the minimum expenditure on professional fees. This puts pressure on the practice to rush the architect through the preliminary feasibility studies and the briefing process, and to produce sketch proposals with a minimum of time and effort.

This may in fact prove to be a false economy. This design will be developed into the premises which will become the home of the practice for perhaps the next 20 years. It is clearly in the interest of the GPs that no corners are cut in developing a well-considered scheme, which has been critically tested against the experience and aspirations of all members of the practice. Unfortunately, if done properly, this can be a time consuming process.

In theory, the sketch scheme can be refined and adjusted at the final design stage, following the approval of the interim cost rent. In practice, changes at this point could mean having to repeat all the consultations with the FHSA or Health Board, and so most practices are understandably very reluctant to modify a scheme once it has received interim cost rent approval. This book cannot resolve this conflict, but it may help practices to understand the nature of the conflict and the type of decision being made.

Budgets and cost controls

A crucial aspect of the sketch design process is the question of budget and cost control. In parallel with the architect's development of the design ideas, it is normal to engage a quantity surveyor (QS) to prepare cost estimates for the project. These can then be reconciled with the budget and the design developed within a cost plan.

Most GPs want to see the cost of the building project covered by the cost rent payments; for some this is absolutely vital, while others may be prepared to spend slightly more to have the premises they have set their hearts on.

In effect, the cost rent is a rental payment, based upon and linked to capital expenditure. The cost rent schedules are set out in the Red Book and are periodically reviewed to take account of inflation.

In theory the cost rent capital allowances have been calculated so as more or less to meet the actual cost of a general practice premises project, and so the cost rent paid should meet the interest on the loan raised to pay for the project. In practice the allowances have always been tight and may at best represent an extremely basic building.

There are considerable geographic variations in building costs in the United Kingdom and even though allowances have now been adjusted to meet this variation, some practices are going to find it easier to benefit from a cost rent scheme than others.

The problem is further compounded by the incomplete knowledge of the level of allowances which will actually apply to the project. The allowances applicable are those which are in force on the date of formally accepting the tender (normally interpreted as the date of signing the building contract). The allowances in force at the time of developing the budget may actually reflect a level of building costs several months out of date. Even during periods of modest inflation, estimated building costs and cost rent allowances can appear to be more widely divergent than they will eventually prove to be. In practice, however, budget estimates can anticipate an annual revaluation of the allowances to account for the effects of inflation.

4 The Design of GP Premises

FEW doctors would need to be convinced of the importance of good working surroundings; the frustration of working from cramped premises with poor amenities can quickly translate itself into tension within the practice team, and ultimately have an adverse effect on the quality of service provided to the patients.

Unfortunately some GPs still view the premises from the standpoint of their own consulting room, and so fail to appreciate the problems facing their reception, administrative and nursing colleagues. Nor do they view the premises from the patient's point of view. Thankfully, such GPs are now much less common than they once used to be. It would not be unreasonable to suppose that any practice considering a cost rent scheme appreciates that well-planned premises, offering a pleasant environment, play an important role in establishing the positive self-image central to a successful primary health care team.

The benefits of good design are not only aesthetic. Clearly, there are operational and economic benefits to be derived from careful space planning, based upon a sound analysis of the size and layout of spaces required to support the practice organization and operational policies. There are also benefits to be gained from incorporating flexibility, allowing for the future development of practice services unconstrained by a rigid, unsympathetic building envelope.

It is never too early to start developing the brief, but it should be recognized that a brief is not just a schedule of accommodation. The process of designing general medical practice premises involves translating the functional, environmental and operational requirements of a complex organization into a plan form which not only respects present requirements, but also recognizes where and how these might change in the future. The development of the brief should allow for refinement as ideas become clearer.

It should start by considering the present operational framework, and move on to future possibilities and practice aspirations. It should at first concentrate on activities and how they are organized both in space and time. Whilst the brief should seek to identify the type of space required for each activity and its spatial relationship to other activities, it should not at this stage provide a detailed schedule of accommodation.

As far as is possible the practice's activities should be analysed unconstrained by the problems of the present practice premises. This is not always easy, especially where work practices have evolved to make the most of a highly constraining environment, as is often the case with the clerical and administrative functions of practices operating from cramped premises.

A good way of developing this picture is to consider the daily activity patterns of all who use the premises, what they do and what they would like to do, whom they meet and what their spatial and environmental needs are. This analysis should take account of the whole period they are in the building, from arrival to departure. If this sounds excessive, it should be remembered that many different people, both staff and patients, use these premises, some frequently, some occasionally, some for long periods, others for short periods; it is extremely difficult, even for those who feel they know the organization well, to take account of these complex interactions without setting the information out in an ordered manner. This analysis should be refined by open discussion with all members of the practice team. Quite often colleagues who have worked together successfully for years have different views, not only of how the practice should operate, but of how it actually does operate. Setting the information out not only presents a clear picture to the architect, but also allows fruitful discussion between colleagues about both present organization and future objectives. In developing these ideas, it should be remembered that a cost rent project offers an opportunity for making operational and organizational changes which would be impossible in present premises.

The development of the brief also represents a challenge for the future. It is unlikely that anyone can predict with certainty the pattern of demand for and delivery of primary health care services in say 20 years time; yet the project now under consideration will have to provide the environment for those very services. While it is necessary to predict the type of services which may be offered in the future, these predictions should be seen as representing a range of realistic possibilities, which the design solution may be required to house at some point in the future.

As the brief becomes more refined, it serves not only to guide the architect in the development of a design solution, but also as a yardstick, against which proposals can be critically appraised. Staff and patients can 'walk through' the plans and ask whether the activities identified in the brief can easily be accommodated. Conflicts which may not have been apparent during the initial discussions can be more easily explored and resolved with the benefit of design ideas. In some cases design modifications can be suggested by such analysis, in others it may prove more fruitful to review and adjust the operational policies set out prior to the development of the scheme.

This book aims to guide GPs through the maze of building or refurbishing premises under the Cost Rent Scheme. It does not attempt to offer design solutions or even design guidance (the Department of Health has recently published a Design Guide for GP Premises), but seeks to focus the GP on his or her role in the design process and bring out those issues concerning the development of the scheme where the GP's expertise is crucial. The following pages consider various design principles, not so much as blueprints for a successful surgery but as issues which the GP may wish to address in the brief.

Privacy and confidentiality

Most GPs would recognize the importance of privacy and confidentiality as operational requirements in general medical practice. A good design should seek to separate incompatible activities, and reduce the risk of the chance overhearing of confidential conversations or breaches of visual privacy. There are two areas of the building which require special attention.

- The first is the reception point, where patients may not wish their discussion with the receptionist to be the focus of public attention. Telephone callers face a similar problem if the main outside line is answered at reception. Since the receptionist is also likely to be responsible for controlling public access to the building and supervising the waiting area (and perhaps even managing the patient call system), there is an obvious design conflict; nevertheless one which can be overcome by a good designer.
- The second and perhaps more obvious area requiring special attention is the chance overhearing or overseeing of consultations. This risk is greatly reduced if the public are not required or encouraged to remain outside clinical rooms. Waiting areas directly outside the door of a clinical room should be avoided at all costs. Clinical rooms should not be provided with interconnecting doors, because acoustic separation cannot be guaranteed and, even with the best of intentions,

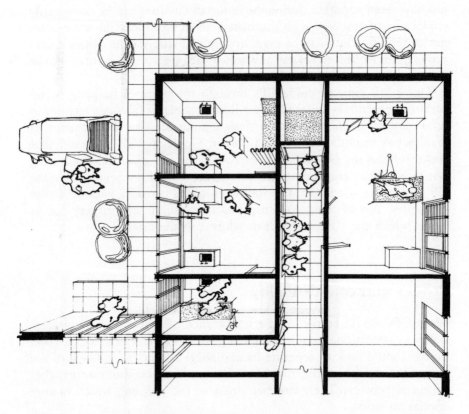

Figure 4.1. A poorly designed suite, with waiting areas outside the doors of clinical rooms, and an interconnecting door between clinical rooms.

at some point the GP or nurse will leave a patient in one room while consulting with another in the second.

The relationship with the outside of the building is equally important: consulting rooms opening onto space accessible to the public should be avoided.

Circulation and communication, security and supervision

Both staff and patients should be able to move easily into, around, and out of the building without causing a nuisance to others. In the case of

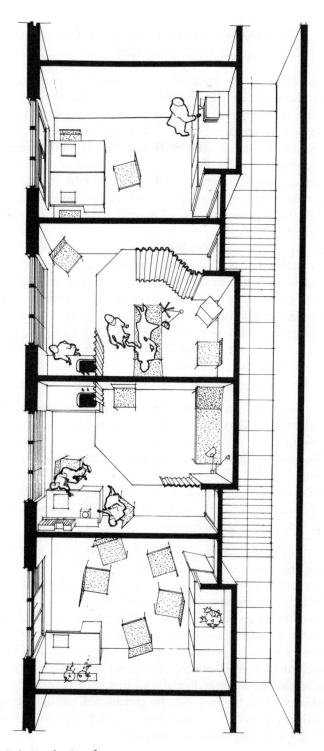

Figure 4.2. A well-designed suite of rooms.

public access to the building, the operative word is 'easy' access, rather than unrestricted or unsupervised access. The premises should be welcoming to members of the public and there should be no confusion about where to go – on arrival when the reception point should be encountered immediately, on being called from the waiting space to the consultation, and finally on leaving the building. However, during their entire stay in the premises, all callers should be under some form of supervision by practice staff. This serves both to maintain security within the premises and to allow patients to request assistance if at all confused.

Up to 30% of callers need not go beyond the reception point. Only those patients actually in consultations and those moving to or from the consultation need pass beyond the main waiting room which should always be suitably located so as to allow scrutiny by practice staff.

In some areas, typically in the deprived inner cities, security will be of greater concern than in other areas. In all cases, security is much easier to monitor if the problem has been recognized and taken on board at the design stage. The location of the reception point is the key factor, and the design should bear in mind the following objectives:

- the reception point should be clearly visible upon arrival;
- only those callers who need to do so should pass beyond the reception point;
- the waiting area should be clearly visible from the reception point; and
- only those callers moving to and from a consultation should pass beyond the scrutiny of the receptionist, although this may not be necessary in a good design.

Security can also be made easier if the building is effectively zoned into those areas used exclusively by staff (offices, records areas etc.), those areas used predominantly by the public (entrance, reception and waiting), and those areas used for clinical activity.

In considering the design of GP premises, the needs of people with mobility problems should be given special consideration. This applies not only to those people with a severe physical handicap but also to those, often elderly people, who find movement more difficult, and mothers with babies and small children. The potential needs of disabled members of staff must also be considered (according to the Building Regulations this is the case even when the practice currently has no handicapped employees or partners).

Figure 4.3. Poorly designed waiting area.

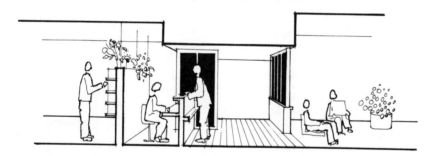

Figure 4.4. Zoning of the building into administrative and public areas: records, reception and waiting areas.

Figure 4.5. Zoning of the building into administrative and public areas: office, records and reception areas.

Meeting these requirements can be a problem where, for practical purposes, accommodation on two or more levels becomes necessary. As this is the case in the vast majority of practice premises, the design implications should be discussed with the architect at an early stage in the development of the brief.

External security must be considered because unfortunately, some GP surgeries have increasingly become targets for theft and vandalism in recent years. The advice of the police crime prevention officer can be extremely helpful.

Economy and flexibility

There are apparently conflicting requirements in designing economically, in minimizing the provision of unused or under-utilized space, and

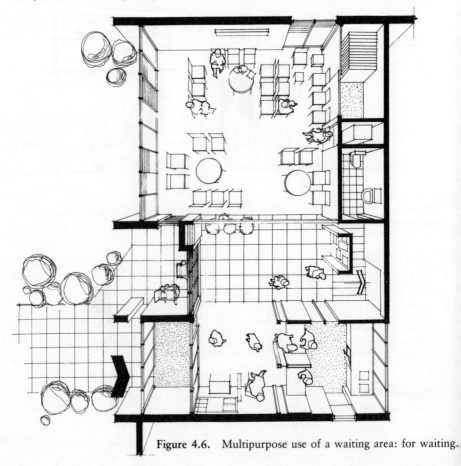

Figure 4.6. Multipurpose use of a waiting area: for waiting.

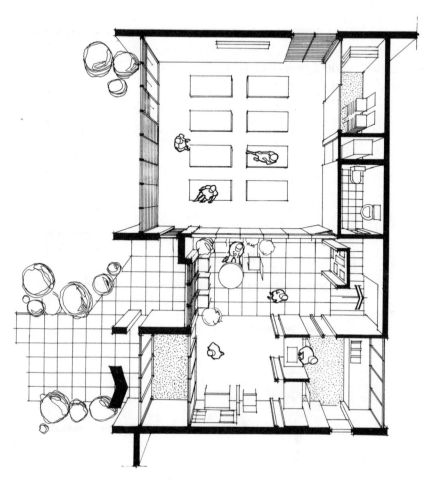

Figure 4.7.   Multipurpose use of a waiting area: for a relaxation class.

in providing a flexible building capable of responding positively to the
future. The possibility of incorporating spare accommodation would
certainly fail against the first criterion.

The key to resolving these conflicts is first to recognize the time
dimension, both short and long-term, in the use of practice premises,
and secondly to keep an open mind on the possible multiple use of
space.

Many health buildings (and GP surgeries are no exception) contain
large amounts of space unused for long periods of time. When considering activities at the briefing stage it is important to consider the

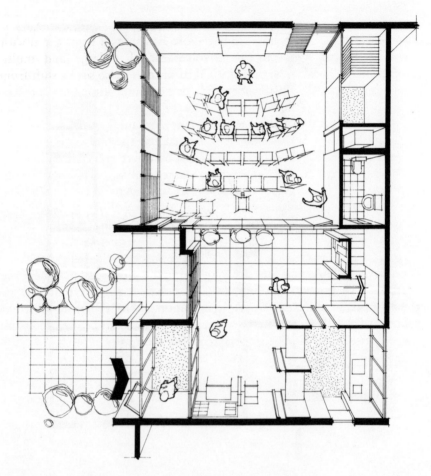

Figure 4.8. Multipurpose use of a waiting area: for a lecture.

projected timetable within which those activities will take place. Where activities require similar types of space and can be timetabled to take place at different times of the day, multi-use of space becomes a distinct possibility. One example might be the use of part of the waiting room for health education or clinic sessions, perhaps during the slacker early afternoon period. This clearly has implications which must be taken on board at the design stage. A second possibility is the use of 'spare' clinical rooms by nurses and outside consultants on a programmed basis for clinic sessions.

The key to a more flexible future is to provide a series of spaces which can allow an easy change from one use to another. Over the last few years the balance of primary health care has shifted from the doctor working almost alone to the involvement of a large and multi-professional team. The organizational balance has also seen a shift from the patient-initiated consultation to the use of clinic sessions for preventive work, although the key element of the primary care service is still the GP consultation, and this is certain to continue for the foreseeable future. Where spaces are tightly designed for specific purposes (e.g. examination and small interview rooms), or where rooms are linked to allow for current work practices (e.g. linked but separate consultation and examination rooms), their potential for independent and flexible use is severely constrained.

These points do not provide an exhaustive check list of design possibilities for GP premises, but they do serve to illustrate the way in which the practice can contribute positively to the process of developing design objectives and ensuring they are included in the process of designing the premises. All projects are different. All practices are different and see their future in different ways. It is important to establish the right relationship with an architect so that these factors can be used to create the premises that the practice requires for the future.

5 Planning and Building Regulations Approval

ALL cost rent projects are covered by some aspects of the Town Planning and Building Regulations.

Town Planning

Basically, Town planning is concerned with the use, type (e.g. house, doctors' surgery) and appearance of the building and its impact on the local environment (e.g. access and parking). Without appropriate consent it is impossible for a project to go ahead, and it is important that any potential planning problems are discovered at an early stage.

There are many issues which affect planning consents. Some reflect national policy (e.g. the Green Belt), some reflect local policy (e.g. the zoning of parcels of land for particular types of use, or the standards of off-street car parking), and some reflect local opinion (whether the planning subcommittee is prepared to approve the proposal). Most of these policies are locally determined and, especially with regard to GP surgeries, highly discretionary. Unfortunately, whilst some planning officers are extremely helpful, others, often because they are overworked and understaffed, are less so.

Before a planning consent decision is taken, local residents and interests must be allowed an opportunity to voice their opinions. In addition, other authorities have a statutory right to be informed and allowed to respond. The most significant of these is the (county) highways authority, which is interested in parking and vehicular access; others may include the Historic Buildings Commission and the National Rivers Authority.

Although it is the officer who prepares the report on the application and makes the recommendation, the final decision is made by a lay committee of elected councillors. The committee also sets the policy within which the officer works. In some authorities the planning officer will be able to give an early and accurate assessment of the likely outcome of an application. In other authorities, officers are forbidden to offer such opinions. An early visit to your planning office might elicit the support of a friendly officer and save much time, energy and wasted effort.

There are several different sorts of planning consent:

- *outline planning permission*: establishes whether this sort of development is acceptable in principle, and can be used to establish feasibility before the production of a detailed design;
- *full planning permission*: the detailed permission to build or extend the building in accordance with the drawings and documentation as submitted and approved; occasionally planning permission is granted subject to later approval of certain reserved matters;
- *permission for change of use*: even where no external building works are proposed, it is necessary to obtain permission if the proposal involves a change of use (e.g. from a domestic residence to a GP surgery).

Unfortunately planning consent can take some time to secure. Although an applicant is entitled to a response within a certain period, this can in effect be extended to several months before a decision is made.

Because of the local political control of the town planning process, when there are problems in securing permission, GPs may wish to seek the support of a local councillor. This should be sought with great care, as not all councillors enjoy the support of their colleagues!

Building Regulations

The building regulations are basically concerned with technical and environmental aspects of the building such as the structural stability, drainage, and resistance to fire. Unlike planning consent which must be considered a prerequisite for the feasibility of the project, the building regulations in general set certain technical standards which have to be complied with. It is the role of the architect and where necessary the structural engineer to ensure that this is done.

There are, however, two areas which have an effect on the design of GP premises: means of escape and access for the disabled (both patients and staff, actual and potential). Both of these have implications for the planning and use of accommodation above ground-floor level. This may affect the suitability for conversion of certain multistorey properties.

6 The Building Contract

THIS chapter gives an overview of the process of turning a design into a building.

Let us assume that we have reached the point where the practice is happy with the design and projected cost of the scheme, the FHSA or Health Board has awarded an acceptable interim cost rent, and either planning consent has been granted or at least the application has been lodged and a favourable indication given. What next? It might seem that the problems are all in the past and that the decisions have all been made.

Technical development

At this point the role of the building professionals is to turn the design into a technical description of the building which can be used by the contractor to price and build the project. This technical description includes working drawings, specifications and often bills of quantity. In producing these, every detail has to be designed and specified to make the intention of the design team clear to the contractor. The information also serves to indicate to the statutory authorities that the requirements of the building regulations are being observed.

Throughout the process of technical development of the scheme, the cost implications are monitored to ensure that the cost plan set and accepted at the time of the sketch scheme is being followed.

If unforeseen circumstances have cost implications (e.g. a trial hole may discover the need for more expensive foundations than originally planned) they should be reported back to the client. Where such costs might be regarded as exceptional site costs the FHSA or Health Board can be requested to agree to an increase in the interim cost rent.

Although most detailed design decisions are made before the scheme goes out to tender, some items, such as questions of interior design, fittings and fixtures, may be left for later discussion and an estimate included as a provisional sum in the tender documentation.

Seeking suitable contractors

Once the technical documentation is complete the project is put to competitive tender. The Cost Rent Scheme requires that at least three tenders are obtained, but on this type of work it is normal to seek prices from five or six suitable contractors who are keen to undertake the building project. Even with willing tenderers it is normal to anticipate quite a wide variation in prices.

If all goes to plan and the successful (usually the lowest) tenderer's price falls within the budget, then the next step is to inform the FHSA or Health Board and the lender, and arrange to sign the building contract. (The tender should not of course be accepted, and the builder should not be allowed on site, until any necessary site purchase has been completed.)

If, however, there is no acceptable price, it may be necessary to adjust some items in the specification or make certain design amendments in order to seek a lower price. Where there is a clear lowest tenderer and the amendments are straightforward it may be advisable to negotiate with the lowest tenderer. Otherwise it may be prudent to request revised tenders from the three lowest. Whichever course of action is preferred, it is essential to inform the FHSA or Health Board and the lender, and gain approval in advance of making a decision.

Building contracts

The essential purpose of the building contract is to bind the contractor to build the premises as specified, within an agreed period, and to bind the practice to pay the agreed sum in a series of stage payments in exchange. All other aspects to the agreement are of a subsidiary nature.

There are several standard forms of contract available and the architect or quantity surveyor will advise on the most suitable one. Most FHSAs or Health Boards will advise GPs to seek a 'fixed price' contract. However, the name can be slightly misleading as the price is fixed only with regard to the works as specified. Where extra work is necessitated at the request of the building inspector (who will make periodic inspections to ensure compliance with the building regulations) or where extra costs are incurred as a result of other unforeseen circumstances, for example the discovery of old drains which need to be removed, the price must be adjusted accordingly. A prudent architect will normally request the inclusion of a contingency sum in the original price to cover such uncertainties. Price adjustments can also result from extras or omissions requested by the practice, and from differences between the provisional sums included for the items not fully specified at the time the project went to tender and the actual costs incurred. These adjustments can be upwards or downwards.

The role of the architect during the building period is to administer the terms of the contract, ensuring that progress is maintained and the premises are built as specified. The role of the quantity surveyor is to ensure that the value of interim claims and claims for any extra work are in accordance with both the contract and the amount of work done.

Interim payments

Once the contract is signed and the building work commences there is little that the GP can contribute other than ensuring that funds are available to meet the interim payments to the contractor. With most forms of contract, payment is due within seven days of the architect issuing a 'certificate' which effectively approves the amount and value of work done. If payments are not made according to the contract, the contractor will lose interest in the project and may eventually stop work altogether and seek to determine (cancel) the contract. As this would undoubtedly have severe financial consequences for the practice, it is important that payments are made promptly. If the contractor is not undertaking his or her work according to the contract, it is up to the architect to take the measures specified within the contract to remedy this. Once a payment has been certified as due, it should not be withheld.

Visits to the site

Most forms of contract would grant 'possession' of the site (or in the case of a phased project, part of the site). In effect, this means that the GP has no absolute right to enter and inspect the works, although most contractors would recognize that a client has an interest in the progress of the works and would not refuse access for that purpose. It is advised that such visits are co-ordinated and accompanied by the architect, and that any observations which the GP may wish to make to the contractor are made via the architect. This is primarily to avoid misunderstanding and the consequent risk of claims for unauthorized extras and variations.

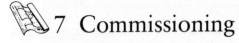

7 Commissioning

SHORTLY before completion of the project, the architect and contractor will compile a list of outstanding items which are to be undertaken before handover. At the formal handover the architect will confirm that the works are complete and will accept possession of the building on behalf of the GPs. In practice, even at handover, certain items remain outstanding, but if they are not sufficient to prevent the commissioning and operation of the premises, it is normal practice to accept possession and allow their completion later.

However, if the project is genuinely incomplete, the architect will not accept possession. Most contracts will contain a clause setting out the sums liable for liquidated damages in such circumstances. Legally, these are intended to cover the costs to the practice arising from delayed occupation of the premises, rather than to act as a penalty clause for the contractor; they do, however, act as a strong incentive to complete the project on time.

Even after the premises are accepted and occupied, defects previously unnoticed may become apparent. The contractor is still liable for this work. Clearly such work needs to be undertaken at times which do not interfere with the operation of the practice. Most contracts contain a defects liability period (usually six months) during which part of the final payment is retained to act as an incentive to remedy and complete these items. Just before the expiry of this period, it is normal for the architect and contractor to draw up and agree with the GPs a final 'snagging' list of items which are then rectified before the final payment is made. If major defects which are clearly the responsibility of the contractor become apparent even after the expiry of this period, the contractor still remains liable for their rectification.

There are two major tasks facing the practice as completion of the building works approaches, and both require planning and co-ordination. The first is the formal notification of completion to the FHSA or Health Board, together with the final cost rent application. The second is the commissioning of the premises.

Cost rent application

The practice will clearly want to receive cost rent remuneration at the earliest opportunity. After months, perhaps years, of paying out for professional fees, building or land purchase and most recently building costs, the project is at last ready to open and thereby qualify for cost rent payments. It is important that these payments are not held up by delays in paperwork.

The actual contract documentation required in order to approve and process the final cost rent application varies from authority to authority. Certainly, all require copies of at least three tenders, and the accounts for the actual project. Unfortunately the settlement of the final account with the contractor by the architect or quantity surveyor can take several months after the completion of the project. This is normal and most FHSAs or Health Boards, being aware of this and sympathetic to the needs of the GP, are prepared to approve provisional payment of the cost rent based upon an estimated final account.

Whatever the formal requirements of the authority, a prudent GP will pass information on at regular intervals and as it becomes available:

1 Upon return of the tenders, and before acceptance and signing of the contract, the FHSA or Health Board should be provided with copies of the tenders received, which in the case of the lowest tenderer should include either the priced bill of quantities or the priced specification.
2 Whilst not formally required under the Cost Rent Scheme, the approval of the FHSA or Health Board should be requested before entering into the contract.
3 The architect or quantity surveyor should be informed that the FHSA or Health Board will require copies of all variations to the contract (architect's instructions), all interim certificates and the documentation in support of the final account; whilst it is unnecessary to pass this informtion onto the authority on a day to day basis, any significant variations to the contract should be notified without delay, especially where they might be accompanied by a request for exceptional site costs.
4 The FHSA or Health Board should be provided with a programme of the work, indicating dates for projected completion of the building work and occupation of the premises. This should be confirmed shortly before occupation, so that any specific requirements the local FHSA or Health Board may have can be brought to the doctors' attention.

Commissioning

Commissioning is a process which must be planned and managed carefully. It should start several months before anticipated occupation, with the preparation of check lists of items to be considered. Items for inclusion should range from ordering and arranging delivery of furniture and equipment, to recruitment and staff training programmes. No two practices will have identical requirements, but in drawing up a list the following issues might be considered:

- informing people – who needs to know and when;
- staff transfer, recruitment and training;
- new furnishings and equipment;
- moving and recommissioning existing equipment;
- timing of the move – staff, records and patients;
- transfer of telephone lines;
- printing stationery;
- contingencies;
- arrangements for an official opening.

The list may seem virtually endless, but unless many of these items are anticipated and planned for, they will cause major problems and disruption during what will, even with good organization, be a difficult period.

8 The Roles of the Participants

MOST GPs entering into a cost rent scheme will have an idea of the role and responsibility of the architect; but what of the other building professionals? How do all these people relate to each other and to the Cost Rent Scheme? There follow a few simple notes which might help to explain their skills, experience and expertise, their responsibilities (both professional and legal), and their services and fees.

The *architect* is often described as the lead building professional, as he or she is the first point of contact between the client and others who will contribute to the project. On small projects the architect may be the only professional involved, but on most GP surgery projects he or she will co-ordinate the contribution of a small team of professionals, while also liaising with the building contractor. The Red Book requires that an architect produce the sketch proposals needed for interim cost rent application; beyond this he or she will produce the final and detailed design drawings, the working drawings and specification notes, as well as supervise the building work on site. An architect is professionally qualified and must be registered with the Architects' Registration Council of the UK (ARCUK). He or she may also be a member of the Royal Institute of British Architects (RIBA). The RIBA offers a clients' advisory service on the appointment of an architect, in addition to publishing an outline of architectural services together with a recommended fees scale; however, both services and fees are negotiable and should be discussed with your architect before appointment.

The *quantity surveyor (QS)* is concerned with the measurement and costing of building work. These services assist the architect in designing and keeping to a cost plan. The architect will advise on the QS services required for a particular project.

The *structural engineer* will, where necessary, advise on structural stability and prepare the calculations required under the building regulations. The architect can advise on the appointment of an engineer, although it is prudent also to inform the FHSA or Health Board, which may wish to approve fees in advance.

On some larger projects the services of *heating, ventilation* and *electrical engineers* may be appropriate in the preparation of scheme layouts and calculations. On most projects it is normal to include basic layouts and some form of performance specification in the tender and to allow the preparation of detailed and technical designs to be completed by specialist subcontractors.

The *building contractor* is the person responsible for the execution of the building works. The contractor operates on a commercial basis and is selected by submitting the most competitive price for the building works. These arrangements are then formalized in a contract which is administered under the supervision of the architect.

The *building surveyor* holds no design qualification, and as such cannot undertake the design work up to submission for interim cost rent. However, in many respects his or her technical skills in the preparation of detailed and working drawings and site supervision mirror closely those of the architect.

The *estate surveyor* (elsewhere referred to as the *valuation surveyor*) is an expert on matters of planning legislation and property valuation. It may be worth the expense of seeking such advice either in the search for suitable sites or buildings, or in negotiations on the price of property. The estate surveyor may also be of assistance if the District Valuer makes an unfavourable valuation for the purpose of calculating interim cost rent. The fees of the estate surveyor are not allowed as cost rentable by most FHSAs or Health Boards.

There are several *developers* and *package dealers* keen to offer services to GPs. As the name suggests they are able to offer a bundle of services under a single contract. Such services could take the project from feasibility to handing over the keys on completion. Some deals relate only to the building work but most include an element of financial management, either by setting up the necessary short and long-term capital finance or by including the project in their own investment portfolio. Although this approach may take much of the worry of the project away from the GP, in most cases it also removes the potential of the GP to become fully involved in the design process. Developers operate in a commercial environment and do not hold the same professional responsibility to the GP as the architect. Any architect retained by the developer is professionally responsible to the developer and not to the GP.

Fees incurred

The Cost Rent Scheme allows up to 11.5% of the basic cost rent allowance towards architects' and QSs' fees, although only 10% is allowed for premises with one GP consulting at a time. Some authorities see this as including any necessary engineers' fees, while others will allow these in addition. Some will allow the fees allowance to be added to the cost rent allowance whether it is spent or not, while others will only allow the fees if they are actually spent. If full architects', QSs' and engineers' services are retained at the fee levels recommended by their professional bodies, the total is likely to be nearer 18.5% than 11.5%; however, full services may not be required from both QS and engineer. In addition, fees are negotiable, but the GP should be careful that a reduction in fees is not accompanied by a reduced service in an essential part of the work. Services and fees of all professionals should be discussed and agreed in advance.

9 Maintenance Requirements

ON completion of the project the responsibility for maintaining the building passes over to the practice. For a busy GP this can be an added burden. There are two aspects of maintenance which can be discussed at the design stage: the ease of maintaining the building, and the cost of maintaining and running the building. These two aspects are not necessarily synonymous.

On completion of the project the architect should make available to the practice a set of the technical drawings, which may be of use if repairs and alterations are to be made in the future. In addition, many architects now provide a maintenance handbook listing the technical specification of all those items which might require replacement on a regular basis. Such items range from a schedule of light fittings to the colour code of painted surfaces which might be needed for the future touching-up of paintwork. The booklet may also contain a programme for planned preventive maintenance.

Ease of maintenance can be discussed at the design stage. It can clearly be enhanced by controlling the number of different items in any category, for instance types of light bulbs and colours of painted surfaces, thus minimizing variability and the need for spares.

The use of low maintenance materials should also be discussed, although there is a tendency for some of these materials to be of a higher capital cost. In addition, although the regular maintenance may be low, the lifespan of many of these materials is as yet uncertain and should be viewed with caution.

The cost of maintaining and running a building is not, for a variety of reasons, easy to project. There are now extremely sophisticated computer programmes available which can project energy consumption and costs. Other variables such as cleaning are under local control and might reasonably be estimated by the practice. However, the cost of routine maintenance is greatly dependent upon the way the building is used (or misused), and can only really be determined later.

Energy costs remain one of the largest components of running costs, and to a great extent these can be affected by design decisions, by the compactness of the overall shape and by the use of better insulating materials. Here there is a direct relationship between capital and running costs. Most GPs agree that good levels of insulation are desirable, but unfortunately they are often one of the first things to go when tender prices have to be trimmed. In the longer term this may be a false economy.

Section 3

10 Preliminary Considerations

Financial considerations

As originally conceived, the Cost Rent Scheme virtually assured any doctor or practice building or substantially improving premises, reimbursement of the interest charges on borrowings of 100% of the cost, always provided that the cost was contained within the parameters prescribed in the SFA. As credit became more freely available and more lending institutions became aware of the scheme, competition amongst the institutions forced down lending rates and it became possible, in theory at least, for doctors to borrow at less than the cost rent prescribed percentage. For doctors in this fortunate position, the scheme therefore provided both interest-free borrowing and a contribution towards the repayment of borrowed capital.

Recent changes in the Cost Rent Scheme, in particular with reference to the definition of the prescribed percentage, mean that in future there will not be the assurance that cost rent will fully cover interest charges on 100% borrowing. It will, however, continue to make a very substantial contribution to the cost of borrowing and will consequently offer a very substantial inducement to doctors to upgrade the quality of the premises they provide for general medical services.

Before a brick is laid

The ability to borrow, virtually interest free, every penny needed for a project should not, however, blind the intending developer to the fact that the project entails a commitment not only to repaying the borrowed capital over a large part of the doctor's working life, but also to very substantial expenditure which cannot be recovered should, for any reason, the development not proceed to completion.

Before a contractor arrives on site to commence work, there will be a long period of planning: a period during which the intending developer will need to employ professional advisers, all of whom will require payment for their services. These will certainly include:

- The *practice solicitor* who will be involved in the conveyancing of the land or property to be acquired and the vetting of any proposed mortgage arrangements. He or she may also need to review the partnership agreement to take account of the anticipated new practice arrangements or to prepare legal agreements between members of a group practice. If the new premises are to include accommodation for other health professionals, the legal basis of their future use of the premises will also need to be agreed. Solicitors normally charge for their services on a time basis, but their basis of charging should always be checked in advance. It must be remembered that only legal fees in connection with the purchase of land or premises and the grant of a mortgage are eligible for inclusion in a cost rent computation.

• The *architectural team*. While some firms of architects may offer a comprehensive service including quantity surveying and various engineering services, many do not, and the developer will be asked to appoint, on the architect's recommendation, a quantity surveyor and possibly a structural engineer and even heating and electrical engineers. The basis of charging for these professionals is likely to be as a percentage of cost or estimated cost, payable at defined stages in their own work (*see* Box 10.1). The majority of this work will occur during the planning stage; 75% of an architect's fees will be payable by the time tenders for the building work are obtained.

Box 10.1: Architects' fees

Work stage	Fee payable	Cumulative total
A Inception	at cost	cost
B Feasibility Studies		
C Outline Proposals	15%	15%
D Scheme Design	20%	35%
E Detailed Design	40%	75%
F Production Drawings		
G Specifications and Bills of Quantities		
H Tender Action to Completion	25%	100%

- The *practice accountant*. While it is not absolutely necessary to involve the practice accountant during the planning stage, it is, nevertheless, a very prudent step to take, so that the practice may fully understand the long-term financial implications of their proposals and so that any VAT charges are minimized, or if possible avoided. The accountant can also play an important role in evaluating the various borrowing options. Lending agencies do not always use a common terminology, and competition between them appears to have produced a plethora of new terms specific to the agency to describe the facilities offered. The same confusion applies to insurance companies and this has to be borne in mind if insurance-backed borrowing is contemplated. The accountant will almost certainly regard such advice as additional to the services normally provided for the practice and charge accordingly. These fees will not be eligible for inclusion in the cost rent computation even if the scheme proceeds to completion.
- The *valuer*. If land or premises are to be purchased, the services of a valuation surveyor will almost certainly be required, not only to establish the price which ought to be paid, but also to conduct negotiations with the vendor over both price and conditions of sale and, if necessary, with the District Valuer should there be any discrepancy between the sale price and the District Valuer's own assessment of value for cost rent purposes. If existing premises are to be adapted, the cost rent computation will allow for either a reassessed current market rent or the value of the premises when originally acquired, and here also it would be prudent to have advice from a valuation surveyor skilled at negotiating with District Valuers. The valuation surveyor's fees are not usually eligible for inclusion in cost rent computations.

In addition to the fees of these professionals, the intending developer will also incur costs arising from the statutory fees charged by the local planning authority and the commitment fee which many lending agencies require as a preliminary to considering a mortgage application.

Box 10.2: Projects abandoned

Costs incurred in connection with a project which is not completed cannot be recovered. A project abandoned after tenders are received will cost a practice at least 10% of the final estimated cost.

Long-term costs

Capital repayments

The capital cost of building a new surgery or modifying an existing building will need to be met over a period of years from the practice income. The annual cost will depend very much on the method of repayment used and the period over which the capital is borrowed. These aspects will be covered in more detail in Chapter 13 'Raising Finance'. Capital repayments are not tax allowable.

Interest charges not covered by cost rent reimbursement

Interest charges on borrowings of 100% of cost, will exceed the cost rent reimbursement either if the cost of the project exceeds the prescribed cost limits or if the interest payable on borrowing exceeds the prescribed percentage. Interest paid on borrowing for practice premises is tax allowable, while reimbursed rent, including cost rent, is taxable. If interest charges exceed the cost rent, those excess charges, net of tax, will have to come from the practice income. The SFA allows for triennial rent reviews and provides the option, at such a review, for the practice to elect to receive a notional rent rather than the cost rent. The point at which notional rent will exceed cost rent will depend very much on the location of the property and the inflation in that location of rents and property values. General experience so far has been that notional rent will exceed cost rent after 9 or 12 years, but there have been substantial variations either way, dependent upon location. For the purpose of assessing the effect of providing new or extensively adapted premises on the practice income, it is probably best to ignore any benefit which might derive from a change to notional rent.

Maintenance

While new premises are initially unlikely to demand as much maintenance as the older ones they replace, they are usually much larger, so that future maintenance charges can be expected to be proportionately higher. Good design can reduce maintenance costs and it is worth remembering that simply designed buildings are easier to clean and maintain than those with more extravagant design. The cost rent is deemed to include maintenance costs.

Furnishings and equipment

It is unlikely that many of the furnishings and equipment from an old surgery can be reused in the new one. While it is tempting to classify as many furnishings as possible as fixtures, by building them in to the fabric, this does add to building costs and makes it more difficult to remain within cost limits. It should also be borne in mind that the replacement of built-in items is likely to be more costly than that of free-standing items. New furnishings and equipment will be a direct expense on the practice. Tax relief by way of capital allowances is available on fixtures and fittings although not available on the structure of the building. Any furnishings which are classified as fixtures and included in the building costs should therefore be separately identified so that capital allowances can be claimed on these items.

Paying for future maintenance and replacement furnishings

The move to new premises or the upgrading of older premises is an ideal opportunity for the practice to consider the financing of maintenance and replacements. These items can be costly, and if not properly antici-pated can prove to be a heavy charge on the income of the users of the premises at the time the expense is incurred. Agreement at the outset to the setting up of a 'sinking fund' into which all users pay an agreed annual amount, will mean that all users contribute towards these costs in proportion to their use of the premises, and that the funds are avail-able as required without the need for a sudden call on the practice income – a situation particularly unfair to new partners.

The need for commitment

The preceding paragraphs have detailed some of the financial con-siderations a practice needs to take into account before embarking on a cost rent project. Having considered these points, a single-handed practitioner can make up his or her own mind whether or not to proceed, but for a partnership, and in particular for a group coming together for the first time to use the proposed premises, there will be a need for all the parties to understand the implications of what is proposed and to share a sense of commitment to the project.

In a large practice, it is normal and indeed desirable for one of the participants to assume the role of manager of the project, but it is absolutely essential that he or she works within mutually agreed financial parameters and ensures that all are aware of the financial implications of events not originally foreseen. Provided that the doctor does this, he or she must be assured of the support of all the other participants. Should things go wrong, that support will include the equal sharing of costs by all concerned. Failure to follow such procedures has been known to lead to acrimonious dissolution of practices and even litigation between former partners.

11 Value for Money and Changes in Ownership

Freehold properties

THE days have probably passed when there was a general belief that investment in bricks and mortar would guarantee a return above the rate of inflation. This belief, fostered by personal experience of the housing market and the reported spectacular profits of commercial developers, frequently gave doctors developing surgeries an unduly rosy view of the profit which might derive from their endeavour.

The value of any building is the price a willing buyer will pay a willing seller. While surgeries were housed in what were basically residential units, there were, potentially, many willing buyers, but with the shift to purpose-built or extensively modified and adapted premises, it has to be appreciated that a surgery has become a relatively small but highly specialized building. Such a building will require extensive and, possibly, expensive conversion to fit it for any other purpose and it is therefore unlikely to have any significant value except to other doctors. Thus the value placed upon a newly built surgery may well be significantly less than the cost of developing it, and it is not entirely unknown for an extensive conversion of an existing building actually to reduce the value of the completed building below that of the original unconverted one. Because of these risks, it is essential for the partnership or group which is to use the new premises to agree in advance as to how those premises are to be valued in the future, if retiring partners are not to lose money or if new partners are to be persuaded to acquire shares in them. While this must be a matter for each practice to decide for itself, it is suggested that an equitable formula is for the premises to be deemed to have a value equal to the cost of providing them or their open market value, whichever is the greater. If this formula is adopted, it is probably better to go on to define open market value. Valuation surveyors frequently have difficulty in determining how surgeries should be valued. Purpose-built or purpose-adapted premises rarely change hands and there is therefore little or no market from which the valuer can draw comparisons. Consequently he or she may need to be advised of the basis on which valuation should be made. Possible alternatives are:

- *Alternative use value.* This type of valuation is rarely satisfactory for purpose-built premises which often have no obvious alternative use. Even if they do, the valuation is likely to be either low because of allowance for conversion cost or, more rarely, exaggeratedly high if, for example, the surgery is in a commercial area where office space is at a premium.
- *Capitalized rental value.* If this method is used, the premises are given a value equal to, say, twelve years' rent. While this system is equitable to both retiring and incoming partners, there are obvious problems if the practice receives a variable rate cost rent.
- *Depreciated reinstatement cost.* This method of valuation is well understood by valuers and, indeed, the Royal Institution of Chartered Surveyors suggests it for very specialized buildings. The RICS regularly publishes tables of average building costs for all types of buildings (including surgeries) and of regional variations. Using these tables, the valuer can compute the current cost of building a new surgery of comparable size and, by then making allowance for the value of the land and the age of the existing building, arrive at a valuation.

Leasehold premises

Particularly within conurbations, freehold land or freehold properties suitable for conversion for surgery use will be in very short supply. In many areas all suitable land will be owned by local authorities, government departments, health authorities or statutory undertakings, all of which are likely to be prepared to sell only a leasehold interest. Most such bodies will be prepared to enter into 99 year leases which will normally provide a suitable basis for development, although the practice solicitor should always carefully examine the terms of any proposed lease. Particular care will need to be exercised if the grant of a lease is conditional upon the satisfactory completion of the building within a specified period. In these cases the practice will initially have to proceed on the basis of a Building Agreement or Agreement to Lease, and where this occurs, no building work should ever be commenced before the practice solicitor has approved not only the agreement but also the lease which is eventually to be granted. When dealing with statutory auth-orities this can cause frustrating delays, particularly if the authority's legal department is divorced from the local office which conducts the initial negotiations, but the temptation to proceed on the basis of assurances from a local official should be avoided if the practice is not to find itself with the alternative of forfeiting all its expenditure to date or being obliged to accept a far more onerous lease than it had envisaged.

While the acquisition of a long lease can be as satisfactory an invest-ment as that of a freehold, this is not the case for shorter leases and, in particular, for commercial leases of, say, shop premises. Unless there is absolute assurance that the lease will be renewed on reasonable terms, the capital cost of providing practice accommodation will have to be written off over the term of the lease. It should also be noted that it is not entirely unknown for commercial leases to provide that, on the termination of the lease, the premises must be reinstated to their con-dition at the grant of the lease. In such a case, the premises become a liability rather than an asset for the practice. This will obviously have serious implications not only for the pockets of the practice but also for the raising of finance, since most lenders will regard such a lease as not offering adequate security for a loan and will require the borrowers to offer more acceptable security. Some will charge a rate of interest above that appropriate for a fully secured loan.

Changes in ownership

It will be normal in most partnerships and groups for the practice premises to be owned jointly by all the owners and the partnership, or similar, agreement will specify that on the death or retirement of a joint owner, the estate or retiring doctor will sell and the surviving or continuing partners will acquire the deceased or retired doctor's share in the premises. Similarly, an incoming doctor will normally be expected to acquire, within a prescribed period, an appropriate share in the prem-ises. The cash that changes hands (the consideration) in respect of these transactions should always reflect the equity in the premises – that is to say the difference between the value of the premises and the total of any loans secured against the property.

Dependent upon the way in which the loans have been arranged, which may vary from a single loan made jointly to all the joint owners

---

Box 11.1: Calculation of equity

The value of a one fifth share in a surgery valued at £350,000 but on which loans totalling £325,000 are outstanding would be:

$$\frac{£350,000 - £325,000}{5} = £5,000$$

---

at one extreme to a series of individual loans at the other, the purchase of the share of the equity can be achieved either by changes to the parties to joint loans and the raising of a further loan of £5,000 or by new borrowing of £70,000 with concurrent repayment of £65,000 of the original borrowing. Whichever method is used, it has to be appreciated that cost rent will make no contribution to the financing of the 'new' £5,000.

While in the above example, the financial implications of the new borrowing might not be great where four continuing partners are purchasing the share of a retiring partner, the situation may be very different for an incoming partner who has to personally raise the required additional capital in order to acquire his or her share. This problem will not of course arise if the value of the premises is geared to a capitalized rental value. If however any other method of valuation is used, a practice will need to give careful thought to whether the choice of new partners is to be governed by mutual compatibility or purely by the ability or willingness of a candidate to accept financial commitments in connection with the premises which are greater than those of the other partners.

12 Keeping Within Cost Limits

THERE is only one limit on the amount a doctor may spend on providing new or improving existing premises, and that is the amount of his or her disposable capital or the size of loan his or her future disposable income can support. However, the doctor concerned that the project will not significantly reduce his or her future standard of living needs to be aware that cost rent is payable only on clearly defined maximum costs.

Box 12.1: Containing costs

Failure to contain the cost of a project within cost rent prescribed maxima can seriously damage practice finances.

Throughout the regulations governing the payment of cost rent, there are alternatives bases for computing the amount on which the final cost rent will be payable. Whenever alternatives are given, the cost rent will invariably be based upon the lower or lowest figure, and therefore doctors engaging in a cost rent project must study with care the regulations affecting their particular project and take particular note of where the phrase 'whichever is the less' occurs. Failure to do so may well result in over-optimistic assumptions regarding the final cost rent.

Purchase of a site

The maximum figure for inclusion in the cost rent computation for the cost of acquiring a site will be the value as assessed by the District Valuer, which will reflect the inclusion of VAT in the purchase price. Such valuations tend to be conservative and may well be below the actual purchase price; doctors must be prepared to employ a valuation surveyor themselves to negotiate on their behalf with the District Valuer.

Particular care must be taken regarding hidden costs involved in acquiring a site. Local authorities in particular are increasingly inclined to seek 'planning gain'. This will usually take the form of making the sale conditional upon the purchaser carrying out works unrelated to the provision of the premises. Examples are the widening of access roads and provision of public car parking on sites adjacent to that being purchased, but there are many variations. The cost of such work is all too rarely taken into account in setting the purchase price and therefore constitutes a hidden cost which normally will not be acceptable for inclusion in the cost rent computation, either as part of the purchase price or as an 'exceptional site cost'.

Purchase of premises not previously used for practice purposes

For most practices contemplating the provision of new premises, the purchase and adaptation of an existing building will be second best, but this option may be forced upon the practice by a lack of suitable empty sites within the practice area.

For this type of project, a very early consideration will normally have to be the application to the local planning authorities for change of use. In residential areas it is surprising just how many residents will object to the establishment of a surgery in the vicinity of their own homes, and planning approval should therefore never be taken for granted. It is essential that appropriate approvals are obtained before the practice commits itself too deeply to the acquisition of the premises and the planning of modifications. The need for approval can bring another problem in its train, as the vendor is alerted at a very early stage to the practice's intentions and, if suitable properties for adaptation are in short supply, may hold out for a higher price than would be the case were the premises to be sold for their existing use. The District Valuer's assessment will almost certainly take into account the existing use, so that the practice may well find that the purchase price is above the figure accepted for cost rent purposes.

When planning modifications to an existing building not previously used for practice purposes, the doctors must always bear in mind that the final cost rent will be based upon the lesser of the actual cost of purchase and conversion, or the value of the site (without the premises) plus the schedule costs. In effect this will mean that if the practice wishes to remain within cost limits, the maximum that can be spent on modifications is the schedule costs for a surgery of an appropriate size (using the Rate B limits) less the difference between the purchase price and the value of the base site.

Box 12.2: Application of cost limits to premises not previously used for practice purposes

A property costs £200,000 and its bare site value is £50,000. The schedule costs for an appropriate size surgery are £190,000. The maximum figure acceptable for cost rent will therefore be:

$$£50,000 + £190,000 = £240,000$$

To remain within cost limits, the most that can be spent on modifications will be:

$$£190,000 - (£200,000 - £50,000) = £40,000$$

Building costs

The SFA lays down cost schedules for practice units of varying sizes. These are determined by the Department of Health by reference to average building costs across the country and are reviewed periodically. The schedule costs which will apply to a particular project will be those in force on the day tenders are accepted or leases signed. Since the introduction of the Cost Rent Scheme, there has only once been a reduction in schedule costs, but increases have not followed an identifiable pattern nor have they occurred at regular intervals. (Tenders for building works are likely to reflect the availability of such work at least as much as they do the cost of materials and labour.)

It is in the area of building costs that the doctors developing new or improved premises can have the greatest influence in determining whether or not their project remains within cost limits. The practice which has a clear idea of what it wants, which makes its own decisions based upon the best advice available, which agrees a plan at the outset and sticks to it and which exercises strict financial control throughout, will have a better chance of achieving its objective than the one that thinks it would be nice to have a new surgery, gives a vague instruction to an architect to build it within cost limits and then, in the course of construction, asks for changes to be made to the internal lay-out or finishes.

The practice's relationship with its architect is all important, not least in the matter of financial control. It is vital to remember that it is the practice which is employing the architect and that he or she must be given clear instructions, which should always be in writing so that there are never grounds for dispute. Required reading for any practice intending to employ an architect is the RIBA's *Conditions of Engagement* or the Scottish equivalent. Many architects will supply an intending client with a copy, but copies can also be obtained from the Royal Institute of British Architects, 66 Portland Place, London W1N 4AD. Careful study of this document will indicate that the services to be provided by the architect are negotiable, as is the fee structure. It will also reveal the very limited nature of an architect's liability to a client.

Ideally, an architect should be instructed initially to carry out a feasibility study (on the strict understanding that the cost of this study will be absorbed within an agreed percentage fee if the architect is subsequently instructed to proceed further). The instructions for this study should specify the site, the accommodation to be provided and the maximum cost for the works (stated as an actual figure) which the practice is prepared to incur. It is important to remember that at this early stage the architect can only make an informed estimate of cost, and that an architect cognisant of local conditions including the availability of suitable contractors, the amount of work they have on hand and problems of vandalism and theft from building sites (which will inflate tenders), will be able to make a better estimate than one with no local experience.

A requirement placed upon an architect to work within a strict financial limit should spare the client from too many architectural conceits which add nothing to the smooth functioning of the building but may qualify it for the award of an architectural prize. However, cost cutting can be carried too far, and while costs may be saved initially by the use of a flat roof instead of a pitched roof, by leaving exposed framing and roof spaces or by the use of finishings of lesser quality, the price for such economies will have to be paid through enhanced maintenance costs throughout the life of a building.

All too frequently, one of the greatest problems faced by a cost conscious developer is the attitude of local planning authorities which may well attach conditions to planning consent which will considerably affect cost. Examples of the type of conditions which may be imposed are:

- the height of the building;
- the materials to be used;

- the need for the building to be in keeping with adjacent buildings (in this connection, the authority may well ignore what exists at present, but relate the requirement to long-term aspirations for the area);
- the location of access roads and paths;
- the fencing of the site both during and after construction of the surgery; and
- the amount of car parking to be provided.

All too often, local authorities are unsympathetic to representations that their requirements are adding quite unnecessarily to costs, and many fail to appreciate that private rather than public funds are being used to finance works intended to benefit the local community. While some architects may be willing to contest such planning requirements, it has to be borne in mind that while it costs the architect nothing to specify, for example, more expensive materials, his or her fee (which is a percentage of the cost) will be automatically increased by their use. If a GP is faced with expensive planning requirements, the help of the FHSA or Health Board should always be sought, since it has an official status which doctors as individuals lack. However, the doctors themselves must be prepared to lobby local councillors and to enlist public support.

While the architect and quantity surveyor will use their best endeavours to estimate costs when drawing up plans and specifications, it will only be when tenders are received that the final cost can be reasonably estimated. (It has to be remembered that not all contingencies can be foreseen in advance, and that even a firm price tender will allow for some fluctuations, to allow for increases in cost due to Government action.) If all tenders are in excess of the amount the doctors are prepared to spend, the doctors will need to examine, in conjunction with their architect and quantity surveyor, the specifications for the proposed building to see if any economies can be made without prejudice to the integrity of the concept. Consideration may also have to be given to a retendering operation involving other contractors.

Once tenders are accepted, the doctors will be well advised to resist any temptation to vary plans or specifications since this will almost certainly involve extra costs out of proportion to the value of the work. It should be noted that the architect does have a duty to advise his client of the cost implications of any proposed variation to a contract and prudence dictates that agreement to any variations should be properly documented. The FHSA or Health Board must also be advised of any such variations.

Exceptional site costs

The cost rent schedules allow for an addition of 15% to the cost of the actual building for 'externals'. These the SFA specifies as 'the preparation of car parks, etc., and (for all but very exceptional costs) site works and off-site works'. The SFA goes on to permit an FHSA or Health Board to consider 'an additional allowance where, of necessity, a site has to be taken which involves exceptional expenditure on site works'.

In the past, this particular provision has been open to wide variations of interpretation but it must be anticipated that the application of cash limits to FHSA and Health Board expenditure will force upon the authorities a much stricter interpretation, and reliance should not be placed on precedents of what has previously been accepted as an 'exceptional site cost'.

Architects' and quantity surveyors' fees

The schedules to Paragraph 51 of the SFA allow for the inclusion in the cost rent computation of architects' and quantity surveyors' fees and expenses amounting to 11.5% plus VAT of the total cost of works, except in the case of a new surgery for one GP consulting at a time, where the percentage is 10% plus VAT, and in the case of substantial alterations, where the percentage is 10% plus VAT although this may be increased to 12.5% plus VAT if the alterations involve a high proportion of conversion work rather than just an extension.

While the majority of architects may well feel that these percentages are low, it should normally be possible to negotiate a fee structure for an architect and quantity surveyor in line with the cost rent percentages. Reference has been made under Building Costs to the need for careful study of the RIBA's *Conditions of Engagement* (*see* page 60), and doctors developing premises must be clear as to what services the agreed percentage fee will cover. Too often it is forgotten when negotiating fees that the percentage specified in the SFA covers fees and expenses. The

latter, if charged in addition to a percentage fee, can add very substantially to architectural costs, covering as they do such items as printing and travel. It will therefore always be prudent, unless expenses are
agreed to be covered by the percentage fee, to establish the level at
which they will be charged and, preferably, to agree a limit on the total
to be charged.

The SFA makes no provision for the payment of an additional fee
should it be necessary to employ a structural engineer. This need may
occur because of ground conditions or if the adaptation of an existing
building involves structural alterations and, in such circumstances,
doctors may well be advised to make representations to their FHSA or
Health Board to the effect that the structural engineer's fee should be
accepted as an additional item in the cost rent computation. Unless
there are very special conditions, however, the design of a new surgery
or adaptation of an existing building should lie within the competence
of an architect and any involvement of a structural engineer ought to be
at the architect's rather than the client's expense. This is particularly so
if the need for the engineer's services arises only as a result of idiosyn-
cratic design. In Scotland, planning authorities require evidence regarding the structural viability of new buildings and some architects find
it convenient to employ a structural engineer to make the required
calculations. This, in itself, should not warrant additional costs to the
client.

It is not unknown for an architect to recommend the employment, at
additional cost, of heating and electrical engineers. Few surgeries will be
so complex as to warrant such additional expenditure which will not be
eligible for inclusion in the cost rent computation. In the majority of
cases, the employment, within the main contract, of nominated subcontractors will prove as satisfactory as, and more cost-effective than,
the employment of specialist engineers.

The fees of structural and other engineers will normally be quoted as
a percentage of the main contract. Should a decision be taken to employ
such engineers at the developing doctor's cost, reductions to that cost
may well be achieved by insistence that their fee only be related to that
portion of the main contract which involves their specialist services.

13 Raising Finance

The need to borrow

FEW doctors will have sufficient free capital to cover the cost of building a new surgery or of extensively modifying an existing building, whether or not it is already owned by the practice. There is therefore likely to be a need to borrow most or all of the cost.

It should, however, always be remembered that the payment of a cost rent is not dependent upon the borrowing of the total cost, and doctors with free capital may well be advised to consider whether the receipt of the cost rent prescribed percentage makes the investment of such free capital in a new building worthwhile. Most practices moving into new premises will have an existing building to sell which in itself may generate free capital.

If the cost of a project exceeds the cost rent limit, very serious consideration should be given to utilizing any free capital, at least to cover the difference between the limit and actual cost. The ability and willingness to do so will undoubtedly make the borrowing of the remainder of the cost easier, and it would be necessary to look very hard to find an investment for any free capital that will provide a rate of return equal to the interest which will have to be paid on borrowing which exceeds the cost limit.

Sources of finance

Over the last ten years, there has been a revolution in attitudes to lending money on property and to professional and business men and women. The lending of 100% of the value of security has become commonplace and many lending agencies have developed special business schemes at rates of interest markedly lower than those available generally to the public. These changes derive from the lifting of credit restrictions and growing competition between banks, building societies and insurance companies for business once regarded as specific to each of them.

Nowhere has there been a greater change than in the availability of finance for surgery premises. The granting of long-term loans for 100%

of cost was once specific to the specialist General Practice Finance Corporation (whose lending rate, prior to its privatization, provided the prescribed percentage for the Cost Rent Scheme) and to individual bank managers who had, over many years, built up a rapport with a practice. The Cost Rent Scheme itself tended to be regarded with incredulity by many lenders, who were slow to appreciate that it provided an assured revenue sufficient to cover interest charges on borrowings of 100% of the cost limits, which in itself made the underlying value of the security offered by the building, if not irrelevant, at least less important. Times have changed, and most banks and many other financial institutions understand the Cost Rent Scheme, although a doctor should not be unduly surprised to find that the practice's bank manager has never heard of it and may need to be persuaded to contact his or her head office for details of his or her own bank's special schemes for doctors.

The ready availability of credit is not without its disadvantages, since each lending agency tends to develop its own scheme which will vary in certain particulars from those of its competitors, so that comparison of the benefits and disadvantages of the facilities available is both difficult and time consuming.

A price that has to be paid for special schemes for professional and business people is that these schemes exist very largely because such people are regarded as particularly good targets for the financial services offered by the lender, which will include banking, insurance, investments, estate agency and even, in some cases, the sale of mailing lists. Such services are potentially more profitable to the lending agency than the making of the loan, and there may well be hidden costs of borrowing even if only in an increase in the quantities of junk mail received.

With so many sources of finance now available, the intending borrower will not go far wrong if his or her first approach for finance is made to the practice's own bank. This, if nothing else, will establish a basis for comparison with what may be available from other sources. The General Practice Finance Corporation continues to offer a specialist and comprehensive lending service but, since 1989, it has become a wholly owned subsidiary of the Norwich Union Group and, as such, no longer has its former independence from commercial pressure to sell other financial services. It does however continue to offer useful bench marks of the various types of loans which are available, against which other schemes on offer can be measured.

Of the high street banks, the National Westminster Bank and the TSB Bank have, probably, the best general awareness of the Cost Rent

Scheme, and both have specialist staff able to give advice to local managers, and both offer mortgage facilities tailored for general practitioners. It must be expected that the other banks and also the larger building societies will, if they do not exactly follow suit, take note of what their competitors offer and introduce comparable facilities.

Some insurance companies, in addition to Norwich Union, have schemes for surgery loans, and details of these facilities can normally be obtained from insurance brokers who have close links with the medical profession. If this method of financing is to be considered, care should be taken to ensure that the brokers have a sound knowledge of the Cost Rent Scheme and have access to insurance companies with an established record of lending on surgery premises.

In a highly competitive market, shopping around for the best deal will pay dividends, and doctors may very well find that their own bank manager is prepared to reconsider his or her offer when confronted with a client who can demonstrate that a competitor is prepared to offer better terms.

Shopping around can be time-consuming and even frustrating, and it may be tempting to employ the services of a mortgage broker to undertake this task. It is, however, important to remember that such brokers make their living from the commission they receive from lenders and insurance companies, so that their best interests and those of the client may not always be the same. The Financial Services Act should offer the client more protection against bad advice than has previously been the case, but the effectiveness of the various regulatory bodies established under the Act is, as yet, largely untested and should there need to be recourse to such a body, more time may be wasted than would have been employed in personal shopping around.

Types of loans

Secured and unsecured loans

Any lender will require assurance that the loan will be repaid and that the interest payable upon it will be received. Normally, if large sums of money are involved, the lender will expect to be offered security for the loan; that is to say, the borrower must provide the lender with something of value which the lender, if the money due is not received at the appropriate time, can sell in order to recoup his or her losses. Put at its simplest, a pawnbroker will lend £50 provided that the borrower leaves, say, a gold watch which the pawnbroker assesses to be worth £100.

In the case of a loan made in respect of property, the lender will normally expect the security to be a Legal Charge (mortgage) over the property. In Scotland, this is known as a Standard Security. This legal document will set out the conditions on which the loan is made and will invariably provide that in the event of the borrower not conforming to the conditions, the lender may take possession of the property and dispose of it in order to recover the loan. Obtaining possession will normally involve legal proceedings, and in deciding how much he or she is prepared to lend on the property, the lender may well take into account not only his or her assessment of the value of the property but also the cost of recovering the loan if the borrower defaults on obligations and the probability that there will be unpaid interest. It is for this reason that, until fairly recently, few lenders would advance more than 80% of the value of a property. The apparently inexorable rise in property values has encouraged lenders to advance higher percentages, but the slump in the property market which began in 1989 may, perhaps, lead to greater caution. In the case of doctors receiving a cost rent, lenders have perceived that the income deriving from that rent substantially reduces the risk of default on periodic payments due under the Legal Charge, and it is for this reason that many will now contemplate lending, against the security of the premises, 100% of the value of the premises or of the cost accepted for cost rent purposes if that is greater.

A property may be mortgaged to more than one lender and the date of each mortgage will determine the precedent to be accorded to each lender should the property need to be sold as a result of default on any of the mortgages. Lenders will normally lend on the security of a second, or subsequent, mortgage only if they consider that there is sufficient equity (the difference between valuation and any existing mortgage) in the property.

The interest payable on a loan will usually bear a relationship to the risk that the lender believes he or she is taking in making the loan. In consequence, a fully secured loan will attract a lower rate of interest than a loan which the lender believes is only partially secured – that is to say, where the loan plus likely cost of recovery exceeds the valuation or equity. If the loan is unsecured – that is to say, where the lender is relying on no more than the borrower's agreement to repay – the interest rate is likely to be even higher.

If a loan is made to more than one borrower, it will be normal for those borrowers to give 'joint and several covenants' to repay the loan and the interest due on it. This means that each of them makes himself or herself individually responsible for the whole debt rather than just for an appropriate share of it. Some specialist lenders may well take the view that the joint and several covenants of all members of a medical practice in themselves provide security over and above that offered by the value of the property.

A practice needing to borrow more than the amount accepted for cost rent purposes must expect the lender to ask for security additional to a mortgage over the surgery premises. Such security could be a mortgage over other property owned by the practice or by the individual members of it (some lenders may insist that all members of the practice grant a second mortgage over their residential property), or a mortgage of an endowment, or similar, policy on the life of the borrower, which has a surrender value. (A new policy has, initially, no value, but a lender may be prepared to accept that it has, particularly if the policy is issued by the lender or through his agency.)

Foreign currency loans

Because of the very much lower interest rates available in some other countries, some GPs have contemplated a foreign currency mortgage. Such a loan involves taking a gamble on exchange rates. It can happen that although a lower rate of interest is paid on the loan, a very much higher amount of sterling has to be repaid when the loan comes to maturity. It is therefore generally advisable to take out a loan in the currency which is earned by the business.

Methods of repayment

Basically, a borrower has the option of repaying a loan gradually over the whole term of the loan or of making arrangements, acceptable to the lender, to repay the whole of the loan at the end of the term.

Repayment throughout the term of the loan

The most usual way of repaying a mortgage by instalments throughout the term is by what is variously described as the 'annuity', 'amortized periodic instalments' or 'capital with interest' method. Under this method, the borrower makes a standard periodic payment which has been actuarially calculated so that the loan will be extinguished at the end of the term. The payments are standard but the split between capital and interest will be recalculated at specified intervals (rests). The re-calculation may take place after each payment or at specified intervals (usually at the end of the lender's financial year).

Box 13.1: The annuity method of repayment

A loan of £100,000 is to be repaid over 20 years.

Payments are to be made quarterly with the interest content of each payment being calculated on the balance of the loan outstanding at the beginning of the quarter and at the rate of 13% per annum. The quarterly payment is calculated to be £3,522.50.

In the first year of the loan, those payments will be split as follows (pence are ignored):

Quarter	Capital	Interest
1	£272	£3,250
2	£281	£3,241
3	£290	£3,232
4	£300	£3,222

The pattern of increasing capital repayments and decreasing interest payments will continue throughout the term of the loan, so that:

in year 5 the borrower will repay £1,920 capital and pay £12,170 interest
in year 10 the borrower will repay £3,630 capital and pay £10,460 interest
in year 15 the borrower will repay £6,880 capital and pay £7,210 interest
in year 20 the borrower will repay £12,900 capital and pay £1,190 interest

---

The pattern of the split between capital and interest shown in Box 13.1 will vary slightly, dependent upon the interest rate charged. A higher rate results not only in higher quarterly payments but also a slightly lower rate of repayment. The converse is true for lower rates.

Where a loan bears interest at a variable rate, the lender will normally recalculate the periodic payment whenever the interest rate changes, in such a way as to ensure that the loan is repaid over the period originally agreed. The option offered by building societies to owners of domestic property, of either increasing the periodic payments to reflect higher interest rates or of retaining them at the original level but extending the term of the loan, is not commonly offered in the case of loans for surgeries.

Some lenders do offer what they describe as 'fixed rate loans' but which prove, on closer examination, to be loans where, while the periodic payment is of a fixed amount, the interest is variable, so producing what is in effect a variable term loan. A maximum period for the loan is set and the periodic payments will be based upon that term and a rate of interest of, perhaps, 2% above current rates. Borrowers accepting such a loan must appreciate that if interest rates remain stable or fall, they will be repaying capital at a higher rate than they perhaps anticipated, and that, since such capital payments, unlike interest charges, are not tax allowable, there will be a greater mismatch between cost rent net of tax, and net loan payments, than would be the case with the 'annuity' method of repayment. A perhaps greater hazard for the borrower will arise if interest rates rise sharply and above the 'cushion' built in by the lender. In such a situation, the loan may well increase because the payments are not covering even the interest charges, instead of diminishing with the passage of time.

One other repayment option which is available from some lenders, is that of equal capital instalments where each periodic payment is of a fixed amount of capital plus interest on the outstanding balance.

Box 13.2: Repayment via equal capital instalments

A loan of £100,000 is to be repaid over 20 years by 80 quarterly payments of £1,250 plus interest at 13% on outstanding balance. In the first year of the loan, the quarterly payments will be:

Quarter	Capital	Interest	Total
1	£1,250	£3,250	£4,500
2	£1,250	£3,209	£4,459
3	£1,250	£3,169	£4,419
4	£1,250	£3,128	£4,378

This pattern of diminishing quarterly payments will continue so that:

in year 5 the borrower will repay £5,000 capital and pay £10,156 interest
in year 10 the borrower will repay £5,000 capital and pay £6,906 interest
in year 15 the borrower will repay £5,000 capital and pay £3,656 interest
in year 20 the borrower will repay £5,000 capital and pay   £406 interest

The example in Box 13.2, taken in conjunction with that given previously in Box 13.1 of the split of periodic payments for a loan repaid on the 'annuity' basis, demonstrates clearly the greater annual cost in the early years of the equal capital instalment method of payment; a difference emphasized if the tax relief on interest payments is taken into account. The lower cost in later years may, however, be attractive to the young borrower who perceives the possibility of higher personal expenditure on say childrens' education at a future date.

Another method of repayment is the capital repayment holiday option, whereby borrowers can pay interest only in the initial years for an agreed period, often of between five and seven years, and then switch to repaying capital and interest for the remaining loan term. Such an option can be particularly helpful when there is a large shortfall between the cost rent reimbursement and the interest paid.

Repayment at the end of the term of the loan

The most common method of repaying a loan at the end of the term is for the borrower to take out an endowment policy on his or life, which matures at the end of the term of the loan and which generally assures a sum sufficient to extinguish the loan at that time, or on the death of the borrower if that occurs beforehand. This policy is then assigned (or mortgaged) to the lender, so that he or she will have the first claim on the proceeds. The borrower has to pay interest on the whole amount of the loan throughout its term.

Endowment policies normally take one of the following forms:

- without profit – normally the cheapest type of endowment policy, it will pay on maturity or death, only the basic sum assured.
- with-profit – with this type of policy, the insuring company will add to the sum assured, at annual or other stated intervals, a percentage amount which reflects the company's performance in that period. This bonus becomes permanently attached to the sum assured and will normally itself attract future bonuses.
- low cost – this is, basically, a with profits endowment policy which assures a sum less than the amount of the loan, but which, if certain assumptions are made with regard to the future profits or bonuses which will attach to it, should have a value at maturity at least equal to the amount of the loan. Because future profits cannot be guaranteed, some companies provide for regular reviews of performance and invite an increase in the amount of the policy to cover any

failure to reach the forecast profit levels. Low cost policies can be arranged so that there is a minimum death benefit sufficient to cover the amount of the loan, should the borrower die before the end of the term.

- unit trust linked – with these policies, part of the premium is used to provide life cover and the balance is invested in unit trusts (the person assured may be given a choice of trust funds in which invest- ment can be made). Because the value of unit trusts can go down as well as up, these policies represent a more speculative investment than a with profits endowment policy and so called 'low cost' unit trust policies will almost invariably incorporate regular reviews of performance, with the potential for a need substantially to increase premiums in order to restore the probability of the policy providing a sum sufficient to extinguish the loan.

In the past, it was common for a lender to accept the assignment of an endowment policy on the life of the borrower which was already in existence, but it is becoming increasingly common for lenders to insist that the repayment is secured by a new policy issued either by the lender or through his agency. The choice of the borrower is even further restricted by the fact that many banks and building societies are now 'tied agencies' selling the products of only one insurance company. The profitability of insurance companies varies enormously, and while it is impossible to forecast future performance, the previous record of a com- pany over the long term frequently provides a very useful guide. Perhaps one of the strangest aspects of the Financial Services Act is that while an independent broker must recommend to the client what is considered to be the most suitable policy from the whole range of products on the market and must be willing to disclose the commission he or she will receive, a tied agent need only recommend the most suitable policy available from the insurance company to which he or she is tied and is not required to disclose his or her commission.

For the majority of medical practices wishing to borrow money for new or improved surgeries, the endowment method of repayment has few advantages and several disadvantages. On the basis of annual cost, there will be little to choose between the annuity method of repayment and the low cost endowment method, although much will depend upon the age of the borrower which will determine the level of the annual premium. Should a practice of several doctors decide that each will assign a policy on his or her own life to cover his or her share of the total borrowing, there may well be considerable disparity in the level of premiums each borrower has to pay. This problem can be overcome by the practice meeting all the premiums as a practice expense, but if this is done, there needs to be a clear view as to who is to benefit from any profits which may accrue to the policies over and above the sum needed to extinguish the loan. Difficulties will almost certainly arise in the not uncommon event of one of the borrowers leaving the practice before the loan is repaid. Some lenders insist that assigned policies are on the life of a borrower, and this may necessitate the taking out of new and possibly short-term and so expensive policies, while the surrender value of the now unwanted policy could be low in comparison to the premiums already paid. Even if the lender will accept policies not on the life of the borrower, difficulties may well arise at maturity, if the whereabouts of the life assured is unknown or with regard to his or her entitlement to a share of any profits.

Because premiums are lower the younger the life assured, it is frequently suggested that a policy to cover the whole loan be taken on the life of the youngest borrower. It must however be borne in mind that the youngest member may well be the least established member of the practice and could leave it for a variety of reasons not immediately foreseen. Were this to occur, the potential problems referred to above would be magnified.

The principal advantage usually quoted for the use of the endowment method of repayment is the profits which accrue to the policy over time and which are not absorbed in repaying the loan. Given that with a sound insurance company, these can be substantial, an endowment policy can be regarded as a good way of not only paying off a loan but also of saving. However, it is worth bearing in mind that future profits are never guaranteed, that terminal bonuses paid on policies maturing now will not necessarily be paid on policies maturing in the future and that, given even a constant 5% level of inflation, the purchasing power of the pound will be reduced by 65% in 20 years.

A variation from the endowment type policy which is acceptable to some lenders is the pension plan policy. Such policies not only secure a pension at a given age but also a lump sum payable on reaching that age which can be used to extinguish a loan. They are ostensibly attractive since, within certain limits, the premiums do attract tax relief. Such policies cannot be legally assigned, and any lender who accepts one as a means of repaying a loan will almost certainly insist that the policy is arranged through his or her agency so as to give some assurance of the regular payment of premiums.

Because there are limits on the amounts contributed to pension provisions which will qualify for tax relief and because doctors are necessarily contributors to the NHS Superannuation Scheme, any doctor contemplating using a pension plan policy as a means of repaying a loan, will be very well advised to consult with his or her accountant before committing him or herself to taking out such a policy.

Some form of life insurance which will extinguish a borrower's indebtedness in the event of his or her dying before the loan is repaid is prudent, and indeed many lenders will insist upon it. This benefit can be obtained from the relatively cheap mortgage protection policies, term assurances and whole of life policies which can be taken out in association with a repayment mortgage, as well as from an endowment or similar policy.

Methods of charging interest

Any lender will expect to receive interest on the money he or she advances, and the rate at which it is charged may reflect any or all of the following:

- the rate the lender has to pay on his or her own lending;
- the cost of administration of the loan;
- profit margin;
- provision against bad debts (the risk factor);
- national economic factors including Government policy.

The method of charging interest rests with the lender, although an option may be offered to the borrower.

Fixed rate interest

Strictly speaking, a loan at a fixed rate of interest is one where the interest rate is agreed (fixed) when the loan is made (or in some cases, when the loan is offered), and interest is charged at that rate throughout the period of the loan. Because this has the effect of committing the lender to that rate over a long period during which there may be wide fluctuations in interest rates generally, this method of charging interest is not popular with many institutional lenders, the bulk of whose underlying funds consist of short-term deposits (e.g. the joint stock banks and building societies). Insurance companies, however, do look for long-term investments for premium income, and therefore may well contemplate making fixed rate loans. The traditional way of making 'safe' long-term investments is the purchase of government securities (gilt edged stocks), and the rate of interest charged on a fixed rate loan will frequently relate to the redemption yield of government securities with a redemption date which accords to the length of the loan.

Box 13.3: Fixed rate interest

A borrower who takes out a 20-year loan in 1990 is likely to be charged a rate of interest x% above the redemption yield of a government stock maturing in the period 2009 to 2011 e.g. Treasury 8% 2009 or British Government Convertible 9% 2011.

With the proliferation of sources of mortgage lending, the term 'fixed rate loan' has become corrupted, and reference has previously been made to its use for loans where the periodic payment is fixed. More commonly, it is used to refer to loans where the rate of interest will be constant for an initial period but thereafter either has to be renegotiated for a further period or becomes variable.

Variable rate interest

It is important to remember that if the interest to be paid on a loan is variable, the extent and timing of any variation of rate rests with the lender. There is a growing tendency amongst mortgage lenders to specify that their lending rate will only be reviewed at intervals and any borrower will be well advised to check the frequency at which rates can be reviewed. This is particularly important for borrowers in receipt of a variable rate cost rent, since this rate is now reviewed only once a year. Reviews of the loan rate at more frequent intervals will add greatly to the risk of mismatch between interest charges and cost rent reimbursement.

It is important for a borrower to know the basis on which a variable rate will be set. Some institutions such as building societies merely 'set a rate' and in such cases, the borrower needs to be assured of the reputation of the lender with regard to rates. Other lenders will specify that the rate will be x% above a recognizable financial marker e.g. London Inter Bank Offered Rate (LIBOR), but probably the most common method of quotation is by reference to base rate. Base lending rate is merely the point from which a specific lender determines the rate at which he or she will lend for various classes of business and therefore has no common basis. In practice, the high street banks will have a common base rate, frequently dictated by the Bank of England, but the base rate of other lenders may well be different. In order to attract business, lenders newly entering, say, the mortgage field, may initially set a base rate lower than their competitors, but it has to be remembered that at a later date they could increase their base rate above that of other financial institutions, with the result that any initial advantage of rate is rapidly lost.

Flat rate interest

This is a variation of a fixed interest rate more common for short-term than for long-term loans but still quoted by some mortgage lenders. Where this method of charging is used, interest on the whole sum lent is calculated for the whole term and added to the capital, and the loan is then repaid by periodic payments representing the required proportion of the total amount.

Because of the method of computation used, the nominal interest rate quoted for flat rate loans is usually much lower than for a true fixed rate loan, and hence appears attractive. In the example in Box 13.4, the quarterly payments are almost identical to those required under the annuity method of repayment, for a loan of £10,000 repayable over 5 years at a rate of 18%.

Box 13.4: Flat rate interest

A loan of £10,000 is to be repaid at quarterly intervals over 5 years at a flat rate of interest of 10%. The payments will be based upon:

Interest	$5 \times £10,000 \times 10\%$ =	£ 5,000
Capital		£10,000
Total		£15,000

and the quarterly payment will be £15,000 ÷ 20 = £750.

Nominal interest rates and Annual Percentage Rate (APR)

The Consumer Credit Act, in theory at least, should give protection against misleading statements such as that quoted above with regard to the interest rate to be charged on a flat rate loan. Under this Act a lender is required to give, in any advertisement or quotation, at least as much prominence to APR as to the nominal interest rate. The Annual Percentage Rate is intended to indicate to a borrower the true cost of borrowing, and so enable him or her to make a proper comparison of the terms offered by various lenders. The calculation of APR starts from the premise that the nominal rate of interest is a true rate of interest only if it is charged to the borrower solely at each anniversary (where the interest rate is quoted 'per annum') of the granting of a loan. Any interim payments, be they half yearly, quarterly or monthly, are considered to be payments in advance of the due date and therefore represent an added cost: the greater the frequency of payments, the greater the added cost. APR is also intended to reflect the cost to the borrower of transactions upon which the lender insists as a condition of his or her making the loan. These will include arrangement fees, the lender's legal costs or the professional costs borne by the borrower, and insurance premiums. Unfortunately for borrowers, the lender may either use illustrative figures for such items or by declaring that he or she is doing so, exclude some or all of them from the computation of APR on the grounds that they cannot be properly quantified before the full circumstances under which the loan will be made are known. This effectively prevents proper comparisons, but even so, APR does represent a far better basis of comparison than the nominal rate of interest. Although APR has to be quoted in advertisements and quotations, it does not necessarily have to appear in an offer of a mortgage, and a prudent borrower will insist on being provided with a proper indication of APR before committing him or herself.

Interest rates and the cost rent

The Cost Rent Scheme provides for the rent to be paid at a variable percentage of the approved cost unless the doctors concerned finance the premises either mainly from their own resources or mainly through a loan on a fixed rate basis, in either of which cases the rent will be at a fixed percentage of the approved cost.

Provided that there are lenders prepared to lend on either a variable or a fixed basis at rates broadly in line with the 'prescribed percentage' of the Cost Rent Scheme, doctors contemplating entering a project which will qualify for cost rent will need to consider seriously the basis on which their rent is to be calculated.

The pros and cons of a variable rate

Particularly for the large practice where partners are likely to change during the currency of the loan used to finance the project, a variable rate ensures that the practice is always borrowing at a 'going rate'. This is of particular importance if any incoming partner is to become a party to the loan to the practice. It is also worth noting that variable rate loans can normally be repaid prematurely, with little or no penalty, which makes total refinancing a possibility.

If the practice has to borrow more than the cost limit, a variable rate becomes a gamble in exactly the same way as it is for the domestic borrower.

The biggest problem arising from the acceptance of a variable rate cost rent relates to the option at one of the triennial reviews, to switch to a notional rent if that is more advantageous. While, at a particular stage, the notional rent may exceed a variable rate cost rent, there will always be the risk that a substantial rise in borrowing rates will leave the practice at a severe disadvantage as compared to a practice in similar circumstances which has elected to remain with a cost rent.

The pros and cons of a fixed rate

Doctors in receipt of a fixed rate cost rent will never be in doubt whether a notional rent will exceed a cost rent, and this is an example of the main advantage of a true fixed rate loan – certainty. With a fixed rate loan and a fixed rate cost rent, a practice can budget precisely for the cost of providing new or improved premises.

Fixed rate loans can rarely be repaid prematurely without the redemption attracting a financial penalty, and borrowers should check the lender's policy on early redemption very carefully before committing themselves. The penalties of early redemption can be severe if interest rates have fallen since the loan was taken out, as the lender will be seeking compensation for the income lost as a result of premature redemption and his or her inability to relend at other than current rates.

Provided that the borrowing does not exceed the figure accepted for cost rent, this need not represent a serious disadvantage for the original partners to the loan or for an incoming partner who is able to acquire a share of the premises purely by becoming party to the loan. However, if an incoming partner, in order to purchase his or her share of the equity, has to raise additional funds, he or she will, if interest rates have fallen, undoubtedly feel aggrieved if disbarred from borrowing all the monies required to purchase the share at current rates.

Rates fixed for an initial period only

The prescribed percentage for the Cost Rent Scheme will reflect the type of interest which the practice will pay on its borrowing at the outset, although there is now provision for changing from a fixed to a variable prescribed percentage with certain loans. A practice which accepts a loan for which the interest is fixed only for an initial period may be at risk that at some period, there will be a mismatch between interest payments and the reimbursed rent. This mismatch may occur at the beginning, if the FHSA or Health Board does not accept that the rate payable is a genuine fixed rate, or it may occur when the loan rate is reviewed or is converted to a variable basis.

Interest charged before a cost rent is paid

Until the new or adapted premises are taken into use, no cost rent will be receivable, but the practice undertaking the work will have needed to raise finance from the moment the project commenced and will have a liability to pay interest on the sums borrowed. The aggregate of these interest charges may be included in the total cost of the project for the purpose of assessing the final cost rent, and it will therefore be in a practice's interest for their lender to agree that interest charges incurred during the construction can be incorporated in the final loan.

While most lenders with an understanding of the Cost Rent Scheme will agree to such a roll-up of interest, some may impose a time limit for this 'interest holiday' which will not cover the whole construction period. Problems may also arise in that while the contractor will expect to be paid at regular intervals during the construction period (architects will frequently issue their certificates which authorize such payments at monthly intervals), some lenders will only be prepared to advance the loan in a limited number of instalments. Where such problems seem likely to arise, it is advisable for the doctors concerned to arrange to open a separate 'building account' with their own bankers, from which all payments in connection with the project are made, and which can be cleared at appropriate intervals by drawings from the main loan.

14 Leased Premises

THE SFA does provide for the payment of a cost rent for newly built or newly adapted premises leased from the General Practice Finance Corporation (GPFC) or some other third party. The possibility of leasing premises will be particularly attractive to practices where the ages of the partners may preclude them from borrowing the required capital other than over a very short term, or where their financial commitments are already so high (perhaps because of the high cost of housing in the area) that they feel unable to undertake the repayment of the borrowing needed to finance new surgery premises.

The true benefit of a leased surgery will only be realized if the lease rent equates to the reimbursed rent. In this connection it has to be remembered that any lease of surgery premises will be regarded as a commercial lease and will almost certainly provide for three yearly rent reviews and for the lessee (the tenant) to be responsible for external as well as internal maintenance. While the three yearly rent reviews are likely to coincide with the opportunity to seek every third year the District Valuer's assessment of market rent, the majority of developers may well have rather different views of what constitutes a fair market rent to those of the District Valuer. If this occurs, the lessee may well find him or herself having to employ his or her own valuation surveyor to engage in possibly lengthy and hence expensive negotiations with both the landlord and the District Valuer.

The GPFC scheme for acquisition and lease involves the doctors being their own developers, and being granted the lease when the premises are completed to the satisfaction of the GPFC. Doctors using this scheme need to pay particular attention to the cost of their project, since any over-run of cost above the cost limit, or the figure accepted by the GPFC, may lead not merely to the possibility of the initial lease rent exceeding the cost rent, but to the GPFC declining to purchase the completed premises at other than the cost it has approved.

Leasing arrangements may also be organized through specialist agencies which normally also offer to assist the doctors with the development, or through a specific developer who will him- or herself construct the premises. Historically, these arrangements have only been attractive to agencies and developers when the fixed rate prescribed percentage for the Cost Rent Scheme has exceeded 15% or some other rate which makes the development an investment markedly superior to the return on a similar sum disposed elsewhere.

The fixed rate prescribed percentage applicable to leased properties is that prevailing on the day the lease is signed. However, any developer will wish to ensure that the lease rent will meet his or her own requirements before work on the project commences. It is, therefore, not uncommon for developers to require the proposed tenants to enter into a lease before a brick is laid. This can represent a very high risk to the doctors concerned and they should not proceed on this basis without taking legal advice from their own solicitor.

Bankruptcy of building developers and of agencies offering a development service is, regrettably, not unknown, and the fact that a developer or agent has previously successfully completed similar projects is no guarantee of continuing financial soundness. Before entering into any commitment with a developer or agent, it will therefore be a matter of good business sense for doctors considering using their services, themselves to instruct legal or financial advisers to investigate the financial background of the developer or agent and to ensure that there exists some satisfactory form of insurance that will guarantee the proper completion of their own project.

Section 4

15 The Rent and Rates Scheme

Acceptance of premises

EACH doctor in contract with an FHSA or Health Board is required by paragraph 27 of his or her terms of service to 'provide proper and sufficient accommodation at his practice premises, having regard to the circumstances of his practice' and 'shall, on receipt of a written request from the FHSA, allow inspection of those premises at a reasonable time by a member or officer of the FHSA or Local Medical Committee or both, authorized by the FHSA for the purpose'.

Paragraph 29(1) of the terms of service states that the doctor shall 'normally be available at such times and places as shall have been approved by the FHSA or, on appeal, by the Secretary of State . . .'

The Rent and Rates Scheme (the scheme) provides for doctors to be reimbursed either the actual rent and rates of their practice accommodation, or a notional payment of what they are deemed to pay. All doctors in contract with an FHSA or Health Board are eligible to receive payments under the scheme, although a doctor with less than 100 patients on his or her list will not qualify unless the FHSA or Health Board is satisfied that the list is being built up.

Before agreeing to make reimbursements under the scheme, the FHSA or Health Board will need to accept the accommodation. This involves a visit from an officer or member of the authority, usually accompanied by a Local Medical Committee (LMC) representative, or Area Medical Committee (AMC) representative in Scotland. The FHSA or Health Board will need to be satisfied that the practice has a properly equipped consulting room with adequate arrangements for privacy during consultations and for patients when dressing or undressing. Suitable arrangements include either a separate examination room or a screened-off area around an examination couch within the consulting room. Consideration will be given to the ease of access to the premises and the movement of patients within them, bearing in mind the needs of the elderly, the disabled and mothers with young children. Adequate toilet and washing facilities must be available for both patients and staff, and there must be washing facilities either in consulting rooms or close by. The FHSA or Health Board will look at the adequacy of waiting areas to ensure there are enough seats for normal requirements; and it will take account of confidentiality at reception hatches, the security of records, prescription pads, doctors' statements and drugs, and whether appropriate facilities are available if minor surgery is to be carried out. Standards of cleanliness and repair of the property and its fittings and furniture, lighting, heating and ventilation, and the fire precautions will also be inspected. It is advisable for any GP to check with the FHSA or Health Board on its policy for standards of premises.

For branch surgeries to be accepted under the scheme, the authority must be satisfied that they are necessary to meet patients' needs. The standard of accommodation will be the same as for main surgeries.

However, in country districts practices providing outlying consultation facilities will not have to meet the same standard as for branch surgeries. Such premises will be accepted for reimbursement only if the times of regular attendance are shown in the medical list. Also the FHSA or Health Board must be satisfied that the doctor could not reasonably give services to patients at other surgeries accepted under the scheme.

Premises may either be an entirely separate building or form part of a residence of either the doctor or another person, and may be rented or owned by a doctor. If the premises are owned or rented by a close relative of the doctor, defined as a spouse, child, parent, grandparent, brother or sister, the authority will treat the premises as being owned or rented by the doctor him- or herself.

Whatever the status of the premises, the FHSA or Health Board must be satisfied that the doctor is making reasonable use of them for the provision of general medical services. If necessary, the views of the LMC will be sought before payment is agreed.

Temporary premises provided by a local authority

The special arrangements in England and Wales for the acceptance of such premises, the calculation of the rental and any cost involved in returning those premises to their original use are detailed on page 97.

Rent reimbursements

Payments

There are three types of rent paid under the scheme:

1 direct reimbursement of the actual amount paid for separate rented premises, premises in rented residences, or premises rented from local authorities;

2 notional rents paid to practices owning their premises or practising in a residence owned by a doctor in the practice; and

3 cost rent reimbursements for new purpose-built surgeries or premises which have been upgraded to become the equivalent of new purpose-built premises.

Whatever type of rent is paid, the FHSA or Health Board will use information provided by the District Valuer (DV).

For separate premises, the DV will assess a current market rent which the FHSA or Health Board will reimburse. Separate premises must be self-contained, and the accommodation used by the practice and any optional rooms provided for attached health authority staff or local authority social workers can be included for reimbursement. Practices can in addition and at the discretion of the FHSA or Health Board provide more accommodation for health authority staff, in which case a rent will be payable by the health authority. The practice, the FHSA or Health Board and the health authority have to agree on the funding arrangements.

If the premises are rented, the reimbursement will be the lesser of the actual rent paid by the doctor or the assessed current market rent.

When assessing the current market rent, the DV will exclude any part of the building which is not directly used for practice purposes, but will include parking spaces for use by patients and by practitioners exclusively for practice purposes. Any rental received by the doctor from a third party for use of the accommodation will be deducted from the reimbursement made.

The current market rent is the rent which the DV considers might reasonably be expected to be paid for the premises concerned at the valuation date. The DV has specific criteria upon which assessment is based, including an assumption that the premises may also be used for any other purpose for which planning permission has been, or might reasonably be expected to be, granted.

Similarly, where practice accommodation is in part of a residence, the payment of notional rent will relate solely to that part of the accommodation used for practice purposes. If some rooms are used for residential and practice purposes, an apportionment of the current market rental calculated for those rooms will be made by the DV. Any room so included as partly used for practice purposes must be used on a regular basis by the practice. If a branch surgery forms part of a residence, the authority will not accept any part of the accommodation as being in dual use unless advertised surgery sessions are held on at least three days a week.

Payments for rent now include VAT when properly charged to the practitioner by the landlord.

The effects of private income

If a practice uses its premises for work generating private income (defined as all professional income received other than from public sources), the rent and rates reimbursement paid may be abated. However, provided gross receipts from private work account for less than 10% of the total gross receipts of the practice, there will be no abatement. If private income is between 10% and 20% of the gross receipts then an abatement of 10% will be made to reimbursements; if between 20% and 30% of gross receipts then a 20% abatement will be made; and so on.

Inspections

The terms of service require a doctor, if given reasonable notice, to grant access to his or her premises to officers and members of the FHSA or Health Board for inspection. The authority may have a scheme for regular inspections of surgery premises, by a team of lay members of the authority and representatives of the LMC or AMC, accompanied by an FHSA or Health Board officer. The aim of inspection programmes is to ensure that the standard of accommodation provided by the practice is satisfactory and, where appropriate, to encourage practices to improve their premises. The opportunity may also be taken to discuss other matters concerning practice organization.

If, at an inspection, the standard of premises is not thought satisfactory, the authority may, after consulting the LMC or AMC, give notice to the practice that reimbursement of rent and rates may cease or be abated until the shortcomings identified have been put right. Six months' notice of such a decision must be given, but the practice has a right to make representations to the Secretary of State against the decision. Such notice is not issued lightly. Authorities prefer to encourage the practice to correct any defects, by offering advice particularly about the financial assistance which may be available under the Cost Rent and Improvement Grant Schemes. A decision to withhold rent and rates reimbursements may then be taken if there is continuing unwillingness to make the necessary improvements. FHSAs or Health Boards can also institute Service Committee proceedings if the failings are considered a potential breach of the terms of service.

Rates and other reimbursable charges

Rates and water rates

Premises accepted under the scheme and receiving reimbursement of some form of rent also attract reimbursement of both the appropriate business rate levied by the local authority, and water rates, subject to any necessary apportionment for non-practice accommodation. Water rates include any additional charges such as sewage, drainage and environmental rates. If a rental paid by a doctor includes a contribution towards rates this will be reimbursed as part of the rental. Also, if a doctor in rented accommodation is responsible for paying rates and water rates, then the share appropriate to the practice accommodation will be reimbursable. Whenever the rateable value is amended, the calculation of the reimbursement of rates, and of the rent or notional rent of surgeries in residences, will also be reviewed.

Water meters

When a practice is building new surgery premises, FHSAs or Health Boards may encourage the installation of a water meter. It is likely that for non-residential accommodation the cost of water paid for on a metered basis will be less than that calculated on the rateable value of the property and it is therefore in the interests of the NHS, and the practice's cash flow, that water meters are installed.

For a practice which is not providing new accommodation, the authority may reimburse the cost of installing a water meter if it is satisfied that a change to a metered supply will produce a saving in annual payments sufficient to cover the cost of installation within a four year period. If a practice wishes to change to a water meter, written estimates of the cost of installation and the likely savings should be obtained. These estimates should be submitted to the authority for approval; if approval is given, the practice will receive full reimbursement of the costs incurred. Reimbursement will be made whether or not the expected savings are actually achieved.

If meters are installed in premises which are not exclusively used for practice purposes, and the water company will not install a dedicated meter for the practice part of the building, then reimbursement will be apportioned as for rent reimbursement.

If water companies arrange for premises to be inspected and charge doctors a non-refundable survey fee, this charge will be reimbursed even if the installation of a water meter is not subsequently accepted for reimbursement.

Refuse collection

In some areas local authorities charge practices separately for collecting trade refuse. FHSAs or Health Boards will reimburse this charge, or the cost of suitable and cheaper alternative arrangements provided by a health authority or private contractor.

Sharps and clinical waste

FHSAs or Health Boards will reimburse charges paid for the collection and disposal of sharps and clinical waste. Many authorities have made arrangements for such a service, either in-house or by contracting with a commercial company, and may make payments direct to the contractor. The authority will provide practices with an annual statement of the amount they have notionally paid and been reimbursed for the service; these amounts should of course be shown as expenditure and as income in practice accounts.

FHSAs or Health Boards will only make reimbursement for what they consider to be a reasonable level of provision of sharps and clinical waste containers: typically one sharps container per consulting room and one per treatment room on a monthly collection basis, and a weekly collection of clinical waste. It is therefore wise to check the local arrangements.

Claims for payment

Forms

When premises have been accepted under the scheme, the FHSA or Health Board will provide the practice with three copies of form PREM1 for completion, two of which are to be returned while the third is retained for reference. Form PREM1 requires the practice to submit full details of the premises in question. Separate PREM1 forms will be required for each surgery. The FHSA or Health Board will send a completed form PREM1 to the District Valuer to enable an assessment to be made. As soon as the authority has received the necessary advice from the District Valuer, the practice will be notified of the payment entitlement.

The claim form PREM2 must be completed annually and submitted to the FHSA or Health Board within seven days of the end of the quarter ending 30th June. In addition to claiming for the next year's payment, the form contains a declaration about the practice's private earnings.

How payments are made

For notional rents, reimbursement will then be made automatically. For rented accommodation and for rates and other charges, reimbursement will be made upon production of receipts for the amounts paid. FHSAs or Health Boards will normally make payments quarterly in arrears, but may be willing if asked to make monthly payments in advance.

District Valuer

The District Valuer (DV) is an employee of the Inland Revenue who provides, as an agent for the authority, all assessments of the current market rent of premises and the gross value for rating purposes. The DV is provided with the details of the practice accommodation given on form PREM1. It may be necessary for the DV to arrange to visit the practice premises to carry out an assessment, especially if they have not previously been used for practice purposes. Clearly it will be in a practice's interest to provide access as soon as possible.

In most cases, before the DV reports his or her views to the FHSA or Health Board, the assessment will be discussed with the practice with the aim of reaching agreement. This may avoid a subsequent appeal. If a practice is dissatisifed with the DV's assessment as notified by the FHSA or Health Board, or with the apportionment of the gross value for rating purposes where some accommodation is not used for practice purposes, then the practice can submit to the authority independent evidence, such as a valuation, for consideration by the DV. In such cases the DV may be prepared to re-open negotiations with the practice or its advisers, with a view to reaching an agreement on the appropriate level of reimbursement.

Review arrangements

The scheme provides for regular reassessments of reimbursements to keep pace with market prices. If notional rents are paid to practices which own their premises, or which work in residences which are owned by a member of the practice, the DV will be asked to reassess the current market value of the property every three years. Shortly before the three year anniversary of the initial valuation, the FHSA or Health Board will send the practice a fresh set of PREM1 forms. Again, two copies are returned to the authority, while the third is retained by the practice for reference. The completed form should show the accommodation in use at the time. The authority will question any substantial changes in the use of the accommodation which have taken place, if it has not previously been informed. The DV is then asked to provide a current market rent assessment which will form the basis of the reimbursement to the practice for the next three years.

If a practice works in rented premises, then each time the rental is raised by the landlord, the practice should ask for a further set of PREM1 forms so that the DV can reassess the current market rental. The DV will assess whether the rent the practice is being charged is reasonable in the light of current market trends.

DVs are prepared to negotiate with practices or their professional advisers in order to reach agreement on the level of current market rent they are proposing.

Review on change of accommodation

If the practice premises are altered between reviews, by bringing into use rooms not previously used for practice purposes or by altering the building in some other way, the practice can ask for the current market rent to be reviewed. In these cases the FHSA or Health Board will first consider whether the change is acceptable under the scheme. Significant changes may require an inspection by the FHSA or Health Board before acceptance. If the current market rent is revised following alterations, the date for reviewing the current market rent will change to the third anniversary of the new assessment.

If a rating assessment is amended, the apportionment of the gross value used for reimbursement of rates and of the rent or notional rent of surgeries in residences will also be reviewed. The practice should notify the FHSA or Health Board to start the review process.

Right of appeal

If ultimately a practice is dissatisfied with a DV's assessment as notified by the authority, it has the right to make representations to the Secretary of State. This right is exercised by writing to the Secretary of State within two months of the authority's final decision. In making representations the practice should supply a clear statement of reasons and any independent evidence available. If the representations are about the amount of payment for a surgery in a residence, then it must be clearly stated whether the practice disagrees with the rent, or the assessed current market rent for the whole of the premises, or with the apportionment of the gross value for rating purposes. Reference should be made to the SFA paragraph dealing with representations.

16 The Cost Rent Scheme

THE Cost Rent Scheme aims to encourage the improvement of the general standard of surgery premises, by enabling practices to obtain reimbursement related to the cost of providing new separate purpose-built premises or their equivalent. In essence, the Cost Rent Scheme enables practices to receive reimbursement at around the level of the interest charges they pay on the capital they borrow to finance a new project.

The Cost Rent Scheme can be used by:

- practices wishing to build completely new premises;
- practices wishing to acquire premises for substantial modification; or
- practices wishing to modify existing practice premises substantially.

The provisions of the scheme are detailed in paragraph 51 of the SFA.

The application

Once a practice has accepted that the shortcomings of its existing premises make investment in an improved surgery desirable, it is a wise first step to talk to the FHSA or Health Board.

An informal view of the proposals and the likely timetable for funding can be otained, but the practice should then make a formal application detailing the shortcomings of the existing premises and submit this to the FHSA or Health Board for approval in principle. There is no need at this stage to have had any plans prepared or to have incurred any expenses, but the practice should have a specific site in mind when seeking outline approval. Before committing itself to further expenditure, it is vital that a practice has received the written outline approval of the FHSA or Health Board.

Outline approval

The FHSA or Health Board considers the application for outline approval in relation to its general policy for surgery improvements and its cash allocations. If no recent inspection has been carried out, officers, members or both may wish to visit the practice to discuss the application before it is formally considered.

The authority has to consider whether the additional expenditure incurred by making a cost rent reimbursement is warranted in terms of an improved service to patients. If a practice is proposing to move to new premises, the authority will wish to check that the existing surgery is beyond improvement.

The FHSA or Health Board will take into account the number of patients registered with a practice, their geographical spread, the services provided by the practice, the existence of branch surgeries and outlying consulting facilities, the surgery hours, whether the practice is a training practice, and any other information relevant to the practice. In the light of the background information and any findings on inspection, the authority will decide whether to grant outline approval under the Cost Rent Scheme.

FHSA and Health Board cash limits for surgery improvements

Since April 1990, FHSAs and Health Boards have been allocated cash limits from which they reimburse all existing cost rents and meet the cost of approved new schemes. (The cash limits also cover improvement grants and the direct reimbursement – usually partial – of the costs of practice staff, staff training, and practice computers.) The authority has therefore to look carefully at every application, and in giving outline approval bear in mind its own policies and priorities. The authority will be able to give an informal indication of whether a project will fall within its forward programme and the year within which cash will become available.

Projects which entail the identification and purchase of sites or premises, or the building of substantial premises, are likely to take a considerable time. Once the details of the outline approval are known, the practice will need to timetable the project accordingly. Almost invariably things happen which change the actual finishing date for the building or affect costs. The authority must be kept informed so that it can consider any changes in the light of its own resources.

If a site is leasehold, the FHSA or Health Board should be told at the time of initial application; provided that the authority accepts the ground rent payable, this will be reimbursed on completion.

The type of project

There are several types of project which may qualify for a cost rent reimbursement, each involving a different method of calulating the cost rent. All the following types are eligible for reimbursement under the Cost Rent Scheme providing the standards of accommodation set out in the SFA are met. If the scheme chosen is not a new surgery building, then the adaptation to other premises must provide a surgery which is the equivalent of purpose-built premises in size and function.

- *New premises owned by the practice.* These are schemes where the practice purchases a site and builds new separate premises.
- *New premises rented by the practice.* These are new purpose-built premises, provided by a third party and rented to the practice.
- *New premises bought for adaptation.* These are premises not previously owned by the practice which are bought and substantially modified to provide the equivalent of new separate purpose-built premises.
- *Adaptation of existing premises owned by the practice.* These projects entail the substantial modification of existing premises owned by the practice. To qualify for a cost rent reimbursement the practice must carry out substantial structural alterations, either by extending the building by at least 12.5 square metres, or by internal structural work costing at least as much as a 12.5 square metre extension.
- *Adaptation of existing premises rented by the practice.* Such schemes involve substantial modification of existing surgery premises which are owned by a third party. The alterations are carried out by the landlord and a new lease and rental agreed.
- *Purchase and lease.* These schemes are discussed in more detail elsewhere in the book, but in essence are projects in which banks, building societies or other financial institutions acquire from a practice newly completed purpose-built surgery premises or their equivalent and lease them back to the practice. These include:

1 new premises;
2 premises bought by the practice for substantial alteration;
3 substantial alteration of existing premises all of which are purchased by a bank on completion;
4 a site or premises bought by a bank prior to development;
5 premises purchased by a bank from a third party;
6 a site owned by a practice and purchased by a bank prior to the erection of premises;
7 existing premises owned by a practice and then purchased by a bank prior to substantial alterations; and

8 newly constructed or adapted premises acquired by a bank from a third party.

Arrangements for lease back are usually available only for groups of two or more doctors.

Local authority economic rents

A further type of reimbursement, similar in many respects to the Cost Rent Scheme, is available in England and Wales when local authorities provide premises for practices equivalent to the standard of new purpose-built premises. Local authorities calculate an 'economic rent' to be charged to the practice, using the provisions of departmental circular LASSL(80)3 (WO 38/80 in Wales), and, subject to the necessary prior approval and other requirements of the Cost Rent Scheme, FHSAs or Health Boards reimburse the amount calculated by the local authority.

In some instances a practice may be provided with temporary accommodation by a local authority; when this is vacated, the practice may be charged for restoring the premises to their original condition, for example if they are to revert to housing use. Restoration costs will not be included in the 'economic rent' charged, but assistance towards meeting these costs may be given by the FHSA or Health Board. A claim for such costs should be sent to the FHSA or Health Board, giving full details. If the authority is satisfied that the work is necessary, the costs are not excessive and the practice's period of occupation was not unreasonably short, the claim may be met in full.

The process

Professional advice

Practices must obtain good advice from the outset. Although sketch plans produced by the practice may be acceptable at a preliminary stage, detailed drawings must be prepared by an architect or other suitably qualified person. It is therefore advisable to select an architect as soon as possible.

Once a site has been identified, or if the practice intends to modify its existing premises, the architect should be asked to undertake a feasibility study. Architects normally charge a set fee for this, whereas if they are asked to produce plans for a project they may charge the practice a percentage of the estimated cost of the final project. If the project then has to be aborted, the doctors may find themselves facing a substantial bill. The architect will advise the practice and take steps to obtain planning permission, something which should be done as soon as possible to minimize fruitless work.

Another important source of advice is the FHSA or Health Board. Whilst its officers may not have professional knowledge, the experience they acquire dealing with cost rent projects is considerable and is always available to practices considering a project. They can introduce GPs to practices which have been through the process, for there is much to be gained from talking to others and seeing the results of previous labours. The practice should maintain close contact with the authority's officers as the project progresses, to ensure no important matters are neglected.

Finance

When arranging finance for a scheme, a practice should open a specific account for the building project from which drawings are made and which is not cleared until the project is complete. This allows any interest accruing during the project to be identified and reimbursed under the scheme.

Design approval

In all cases, the FHSA or Health Board needs to be satisfied that the project is consistent with the SFA recommendations and either provides separate purpose-built premises or a surgery of equivalent standard created through alterations to existing premises.

The FHSA or Health Board will wish to ensure that all necessary rooms are provided and are of the right size, that the layout of rooms ensures good working arrangements, and that patient flow, confidentiality and privacy are taken into account. The authority may seek independent expert medical advice in assessing the proposals. The general standards of practice accommodation required are as follows.

Accommodation

- *Consulting rooms*. A suitable size for a combined consulting and examination room is about 11 square metres, as this allows space for the usual furnishing including an examination couch. If a separate examination room is provided, a consulting room of not less than 9.5 square metres is acceptable. If a practitioner is a recognized teacher of medical students, a larger consulting room of up to some 13.5 square metres is desirable.

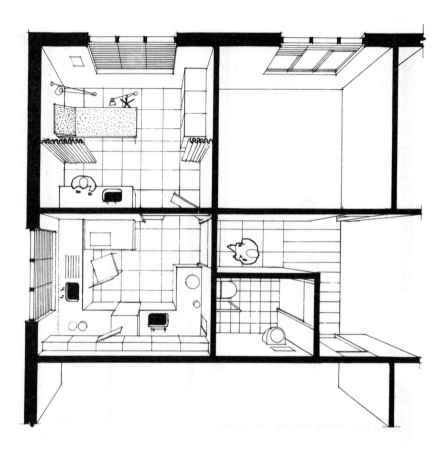

Figure 16.1. Treatment area, small to medium-sized practice.

- *Examination rooms.* An examination room must be large enough to contain an examination couch 1.85 metres in length and rooms smaller than 4.5 square metres are unlikely to be satisfactory. If the room is to be used for teaching purposes, it should be some 6.7 square metres.
- *Treatment room.* A room of 17.5 square metres provides space for a free-standing couch and reasonable arrangements for the nurse working there. Rooms of less than 9.5 square metres will be of limited usefulness.
- *Waiting space.* If a full appointments system is in operation seven seats are appropriate for a single consulting room and twelve seats for

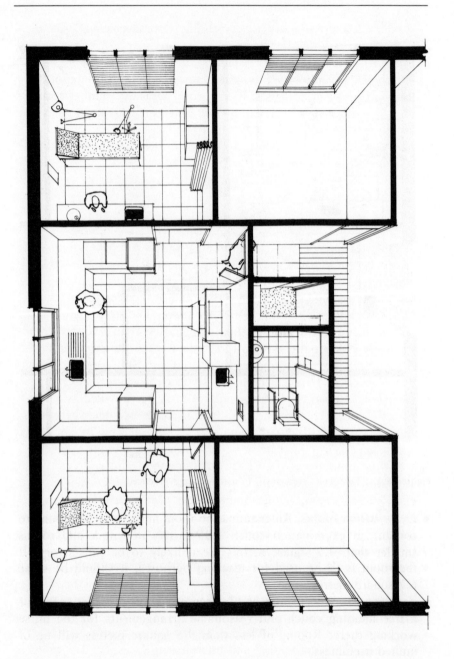

Figure 16.2.   Treatment area, large practice.

two; otherwise five seats per consulting room are usually sufficient. Patients waiting for the treatment room or to see other members of the practice team will also require seating.

If there is no appointments system, one seat is appropriate for every 200 patients using premises. In very rural areas the number required may be rather fewer, down to one seat per 300 patients. These estimates are based on the traditional practice of ten surgery sessions per week, and if the number of surgery sessions is increased or sessions are staggered, fewer seats may be needed.

To assess the area required, not less than one square metre per seat should be allowed. Depending on the shape of the area and the number of points of access, an additional allowance of up to 30% may be needed for circulation.

- *Toilet facilities*. Patients using the premises should have the use of a lavatory with washing facilities. Separate staff lavatories should be considered. Basins with a running water supply must be available in the consulting or examination rooms and in the treatment room.
- *Office, reception and records storage space*. The space required for reception and record storage should be not less than 2 square metres for every 1,000 patients whose records are kept at those premises. Additional space for typing and secretarial work is needed and should be not less than 1 square metre per 1,000 patients. In small premises the whole allowance, 3 square metres, may be provided as a single area. The areas recommended allow for storage of folders containing A4 medical records. In larger premises it is preferable to isolate the typing area to minimize noise disturbance. With average numbers of staff the requirements of the Offices, Shops and Railway Premises Act 1963 will be satisfied by the above standards. This Act requires staff employed for more than 21 hours a week each to have a floor space of 4 square metres (or a room capacity of 11.5 cubic metres if the ceiling is lower than 3 metres). Sanitary and washing facilities must be provided for practice staff.
- *Common room*. A common room for all members of the practice team is a valuable asset. An allowance of 1.5 square metres should be made for each person likely to be present at one time, with a minimum of 9.5 square metres.
- *Rooms for attached staff*. Attached health visitors should be provided with office accommodation and interviewing facilities. A combined office and interview room should preferably be 11 square metres in size and should not be less than 9.5 square metres. Authorities may

consult with the appropriate Nursing Officer (District Nursing Officer in England, Chief Administrative Nursing Officer in Wales) and Director of Social Services to ascertain their requirements.

- *Interview rooms*. In larger premises, it is useful to have a dedicated interview room of not less than 7.5 square metres which can be used by members of the practice and by attached health visitors or social workers.
- *Other facilities*. Consideration should be given to the provision of car parking, a covered pram shelter, storage space, a cleaner's store with suitable sink, and the heating system.

Other considerations

- *Privacy*. Privacy of conversation is absolutely essential and during the design stage must be a very high priority for the practice and its architect. It is almost impossible to ensure privacy if waiting patients are seated next to the doors of consulting rooms or if doors communicate directly between rooms which are both in use for consultations or examinations. A reception counter opening directly onto the waiting area makes it difficult to ensure privacy between receptionists and patients or to prevent telephone conversations being overheard. The need to oversee the waiting areas can be met by means of a glazed movable hatch.
- *Disabled persons*. Whenever possible, and invariably in the case of a new building, the need for access by disabled persons using wheelchairs should be considered. One lavatory should be suitable for use by wheelchair patients.

The maximum cost limit schedules in the SFA vary according to the number of GPs consulting at a time. These provide an overall size limit for the practice unit, including: office, reception and record storage areas, waiting space, consulting and examination rooms, a treatment room, lavatories, storage space, circulation areas, and in the case of practices larger than two GPs, a common room.

In addition to the practice unit, optional additional rooms are allowed: interview rooms and offices for attached or practice nursing staff, a dispensary, and for one or two doctor units a common room. The maximum gross areas, within external walls, permissible for reimbursement purposes, for various sizes of practices are shown in Box 16.1.

Box 16.1: Optional additional rooms										
	Number of GPs consulting at a time									
	1	2	3	4	5	6	7	8	9	10
	m^2	m^2	m^2	m^2	m^2	m^2	m^2	m^2	m^2	m^2
Practice unit	88	164	249	307	367	420	473	525	578	648
Optional additional rooms (allowing for circulation):										
Attached or practice nursing staff interview	14	14	14	14	28	28	28	28	28	28
Attached or practice nursing staff office	14	14	23	28	35	35	35	35	35	35
Dispensary	14	14	23	23	*	*	*	*	*	*
Common room	17	17	–	–	–	–	–	–	–	–
Consulting/ examination room for GP trainee	11	11	11	11	11	11	11	11	11	11

as appropriate for size of practice

New purpose-built premises should therefore be designed as closely as possible to these limits. If new premises are built significantly smaller than these maximum sizes (i.e. more than 5% smaller), the maximum cost rent reimbursement payable will be reduced. If the premises are larger than the maximum sizes, it is unlikely that the cost rent reimbursement will cover the entire cost of the project.

To ensure that the practice receives timely advice about the project the FHSA or Health Board must see the plans at an early stage. Authority staff, sometimes with a medical adviser, will visit the practice to discuss preliminary plans, although it is always helpful to put something on paper before such a visit. It is useful if the practice's architect is present to add a professional view of the practicability of the suggestions made.

District Valuer

Once the practice has identified a site to purchase, the FHSA or Health
Board can obtain from the District Valuer a confidential assessment of
the current market value of that site, including VAT where there is an
actual liability to VAT, including under the self-supply VAT regulations. To provide this the DV will require an outline sketch plan of
the site from the practice. The provision of this confidential assessment
will enable the authority to advise the practice formally that the project
is acceptable for cost rent reimbursement, and to issue a written offer
together with an estimate of the amount of cost rent reimbursement.

If the project involves purchasing premises for substantial modification, the DV will be asked to assess the current market value of the
site alone and the premises including the site. If existing premises of the
practice are to be modified, the DV will be asked for an assessment of
the current market value of the site of the premises when originally
acquired by the practice, and will also be asked to provide a reassessment of the current market rent of the existing premises as at the date
the practice accepts the tender for the work. These assessments are used
to calculate interim cost rents, but as will be seen in Chapter 18 the
method of calculation of the cost rent varies according to the type of
project.

Acquisition of land

When details of the interim cost rent have been received, the practice
will be in a position to assess whether the proposal is financially sound.
In particular, the practice will want to be assured that the DV's assessment of the current market value of the site is not significantly below
the asking price, because the final cost rent reimbursement will utilize
the lower of these two figures. The actual site cost includes VAT which
is properly charged, or the net amount of VAT necessarily incurred
under the self-supply VAT regulations.

The practice will not wish to purchase the site too far in advance of
the start of building work, because there is no financial return until the
whole project is completed.

The cost limits – interim cost rent

Having first given its outline approval, and then its subsequent approval
of the plans of the proposed premises in the light of advice from the DV,

the FHSA or Health Board will next advise the practice whether the detailed project is acceptable for a cost rent reimbursement. If so, it will issue a formal written offer which will include the interim cost rent. The interim cost rent is an estimate of the final cost rent reimbursement the practice will receive. Of necessity it can take into account only the factors known at that time, and the prescribed percentage and cost limits used are those in force at the date of the calculation. This is unlikely to produce the precise figure of the final cost rent, which will use figures current at the date tenders are accepted. However, it will give an idea of the reimbursement, and so enable the practice to judge whether the scheme is financially viable or can be made so by amendment.

Whenever any variation from the information originally given to the FHSA or Health Board occurs, in the form of changed plans, or additional work arising from site problems, or perhaps through a requirement of the planning authority, the FHSA or Health Board should be informed immediately. If the change is accepted, a revised interim cost rent will be issued.

Method of calculation

There are 13 different scenarios for cost rent projects, ranging from new purpose-built premises on a greenfield site, through adaptations of existing premises which are owned or rented by the practice, to a variety of arrangements for banks or other financial institutions to purchase the property and lease it back to the doctors. Each type of project has its own method of calculation of the cost rent reimbursement and the precise basis of each is given in Chapter 18. The basis of all these calculations is found in the maximum cost limit schedule in the SFA. The interim cost rent is calculated by applying the prescribed percentage to the maximum cost limit together with the DV's assessment of the site value. This calculation results in an estimate of the annual cost rent reimbursement the practice can expect to receive when the project is completed.

Prescribed percentage

The prescribed percentage is an interest rate determined by the Department of Health and notified to the FHSA or Health Board. Two figures are set, a fixed interest rate and a variable interest rate. The fixed rate is updated quarterly and the variable rate annually by the Department, in line with movements in interest rates.

For owner occupiers, the prescribed percentage will be the appropriate interest rate prevailing on the date when the tender for the project is accepted. The rate will be the variable interest rate unless the practice is financing the scheme wholly or mainly:

- through a fixed rate loan for the major part of the cost of the project;
- through a loan on a fixed rate basis, but with the option of switching to a variable rate; or
- from its own money.

In these cases the fixed interest rate will apply, although in the second case only for so long as the loan remains on a fixed rate basis.

If the prescribed percentage used is the variable interest rate, the final cost rent paid by the FHSA or Health Board will vary in line with changes in the variable interest rate, whereas a practice receiving reimbursement based on a fixed rate prescribed percentage will have its cost rent fixed for the duration of the loan.

If a practice is leasing premises from a third party, the prescribed percentage used will be the fixed interest rate prevailing on the date the lease for the premises is signed.

Practices qualifying for reimbursement based on a fixed interest rate must apply in writing to the authority before the date the tenders are accepted, confirming the basis of financing the scheme. If the financial arrangements have not been finalized by then, the outline intentions must be notified to the authority before that date and confirmed as soon as possible, certainly within six months. In default of a proper notification, the variable interest rate will be applied to the cost rent reimbursement.

Maximum cost limits

The SFA provides schedules of accommodation for varying sizes of practices, which set a maximum size for which reimbursement may be claimed and the appropriate cost limit. Two costs are shown, Rate A which is applicable to new premises and Rate B, a lower rate which relates to alterations to existing premises. These are known as the maximum cost limit schedules.

There are four bands of cost limits, each containing Rates A and B. These bands relate to the building costs in different areas of the country.

Band 1, the lowest, applies in those areas where building costs are relatively cheap, whereas Band 4 applies in the more expensive areas, such as London. The bands are based upon the Building Costs Information Service (BCIS) Tender Price Index produced by the Royal Institution of Chartered Surveyors and are reviewed annually each April. The cost rent cost limits are also reviewed annually in April and are based upon the BCIS All-In Tender Price Index.

Factors affecting the maximum cost limit

- *Training practice*. Where a member of the practice undertaking a cost rent project is an approved trainer, an additional room may be provided for the trainee. This additional room will be the size of an ordinary consulting room, but the practice may wish to increase the size of the trainer's room by around 2.5 square metres to enable him or her to consult with the trainee observing. An additional allowance will be added to the calculation as an optional additional room.
- *Exceptional site costs*. If a practice has no option but to build on a site which involves exceptional expenditure on site works, an application may be made to the FHSA or Health Board for an additional allowance to be added to the cost rent reimbursement to take account of this. Full documentation of the difficulties with the site will be needed, and the authority will have to be assured that, in view of the extra costs that are being generated, it would not have been preferable to have sought an alternative site. Exceptional site costs may cover such items as extraordinary structural work or the demolition of redundant structures on the site.
- *Message taker's accommodation*. The Cost Rent Scheme does not normally allow for residential accommodation. However, where a practice includes within new separate purpose-built premises residential accommodation for a person other than a doctor, with the duty of answering emergency calls for patients outside surgery hours, its cost may be included within the reimbursement if considered reasonable. The additional amount will be calculated on a cost per square metre basis as optional additional rooms.

Calculation of interim cost rent

The following example in Box 16.2, shows the calculation of an interim cost rent reimbursement for a three GP unit. The practice in the example is a training practice in a rural area, dispensing for a considerable number of its patients. It is therefore providing a trainee suite of 11 square metres and a dispensary of 18 square metres. The main practice unit is 225 square metres. There is an interview room for the use of attached nursing staff of 14 square metres and an office for their use of 16 square metres. The project is to build a new purpose-built unit on a site costing £50,000 for which exceptional site costs of £25,000 have been approved following the discovery of a uncapped mine shaft under the site.

Based on the factors in Box 16.2, this practice would be likely to receive an estimated cost rent reimbursement of £44,089 per annum. Using this and the provisional costings provided by the architect, the practice will be able to see whether it can contain costs within the allowable limits and whether the expected reimbursement makes the project financially viable.

The final details

Tenders

Having decided to proceed with the project on the basis of the interim cost rent and the outline approval, the practice can proceed to tender. A minimum of three competitive tenders should be obtained and submitted. If there is difficulty in obtaining three tenders, the authority should be consulted and exceptionally may be prepared to accept less.

Bills of quantity or specification

In addition to seeing the tender documents, the FHSA or Health Board should see the bills of quantity or specification for the building work, so that it can assess whether any work incorporated in the project is ineligible for cost rent reimbursement.

With new premises it is unlikely that much work would be ineligible for inclusion, but where the project involves substantial alterations to existing premises there may be some elements which do not qualify. As a general rule any building work, built-in cupboards, units, benches and seating will be eligible for inclusion as will carpets, carpeting and carpet tiles covering the floors of newly constructed rooms, or in rooms undergoing substantial structural alteration if they are fully fitted and fixed to the floor. Curtains and rails around examination

---

Box 16.2: Interim cost rent calculation: three doctor training practice

Maximum cost limit schedule

1	Practice unit			
	for 249 m^2		£147,200	
	actual size 225 m^2 is more than 5%			
	below 249 m^2 therefore deduct 24 m^2			
	@ £488 per m^2		£ 11,712	
				£135,488

2	Optional rooms			
	a) attached staff interview	14 m^2		
	b) attached staff office	16 m^2		
	c) dispensary	18 m^2		
	d) trainee suite	11 m^2		
		59 m^2 × £488 per m^2	£ 28,792	

3	Allowance for externals	15% of 1 and 2	£ 24,642
3a	Exceptional site costs		£ 25,000
4	Allowance for architect's and quantity surveyor's fees 11.5% of **1,2,3** and **3a** (less VAT)		£ 20,937
	+ VAT on 4		£ 3,664
5	Planning costs		£ 500
	Maximum cost limit		£239,023
	plus site value		£ 50,000
	+ VAT		
			£289,023

Multiplied by variable prescribed percentage (11.5%):

Annual interim (estimated) cost rent reimbursement   £ 33,238

---

couches are also eligible, but not curtains and rails at windows. Work regarded as repair or maintenance of existing premises cannot be included in the reimbursement, nor can redecoration of existing rooms unless they have had major work on them which has rendered redecoration necessary. Items of equipment, even if included in the specification, will be ineligible for inclusion in the cost rent reimbursement.

Planning approval

The FHSA or Health Board will need to see documentation relating to building regulations and the granting of planning permission.

Ready to go ahead

When the necessary documentation has been received, the FHSA or Health Board will be able to provide a more accurate assessment of the cost rent reimbursement likely to be payable, by taking into account the lowest tender and excluding any ineligible items. Any subsequent alterations to the project or additional items of work must be brought to the attention of the authority. Approved additional amounts are likely to be reimbursable if the total cost of the project remains within the maximum allowed.

All is set for the project to commence but the practice must advise the FHSA or Health Board of the date on which the tender is ultimately accepted.

Self-supply and VAT registration

Any doctor developing new premises where the project has a total cost (including land) of more than £100,000 must register for VAT, as must doctors in certain circumstances when extending, enlarging or reconstructing an existing building, where the total value of the self-supply is not less than £100,000. Self-supply occurs when a doctor supplies premises to him- or herself, on completion of the project or on first occupation, whichever is earlier. The doctor is classed as a developer of premises, and the self-supply is subject to VAT at the standard rate.

A doctor or partnership must apply for registration within 30 days of the self-supply, or a financial penalty can be imposed. However, if the registration occurs at the start of the development, cash flow can be improved by recovering the VAT paid out to contractors and professional advisers.

Doctors should apply for VAT registration to the local VAT office. This is done on form VAT 1 and all partnerships should also submit form VAT 2. A notice of receipt of the application should be received, followed by notification of registration. It is essential to seek advice from an accountant, both on the registration process and on the completion of quarterly VAT returns.

It is important to keep a tight rein on invoices as they are paid and to bring them to account promptly because returns of VAT paid and reclaimed from Customs are made quarterly. The returns must be submitted on time as there are penalties for late submission.

Submission of quarterly VAT returns allows recovery of VAT paid out on the project during development. This will include any VAT paid on the cost of the land as well as all the standard-rated supplies of goods and services received in the course of development, such as contractors' work, architects' and solicitors' fees and all the other incidental costs. VAT incurred on services from architects and others received up to six months prior to registration, and on goods on hand and to be used in the development at the time of registration, is recoverable on the first VAT return submitted.

The provision of health care and general practice is an exempt supply, in relation to which no VAT can be reclaimed. Customs can ask to see accounts relating to the practice to check that none of the VAT relating to the exempt provision of health care is reclaimed inadvertently.

At the time of the self-supply the doctor will have to pay VAT on the total value of the project. This will usually be the historic cost of the land together with the standard-rated development costs. Any VAT paid but not already recovered in relation to the project may be reclaimed at the same time on the VAT return, and netted off against the VAT to be paid.

After all the VAT paid out on the project has been reclaimed, the doctor or partnership should deregister because the business then reverts to making exempt supplies only. The timing of deregistration is important and the practice accountant's advice should be sought. It is usual practice to retain a proportion of the builder's charges until the building has been occupied for six months and the architect has made a final inspection with his or her client. It may be that the VAT paid out on the project has not all been reclaimed due to late receipt of invoices. Customs and Excise should be approached to allow the VAT registration to continue until such late invoices have been received and reclaimed before the doctor deregisters.

In summary, VAT is paid out to contractors and reclaimed from customs quarterly. VAT on the self-supply of the premises is then paid to customs at the end of the project. This VAT is repaid to the doctor via the FHSA or Health Board as part of the Cost Rent Scheme within the limits of the schedules.

Although VAT is reclaimed as the project proceeds, and it may appear that some VAT is actually saved, in the final analysis VAT will have been levied on all the costs of the project at the standard rate.

17 The Improvement Grant Scheme

Eligibility of doctors

THE Improvement Grant Scheme enables practices to claim from the FHSA or Health Board a grant towards the cost of surgery improvements. To be eligible to receive a grant, a doctor should normally be providing unrestricted general medical services and have 500 or more patients on his or her NHS list (or an average of 500 for partnerships), except that in rural areas, the figures are reduced to 350 or more patients. Grants may also be paid to doctors who are expected to build up their lists to these levels over the next year or so.

Cash limits

An FHSA or Health Board will assess an application for an improvement grant according to its own priorities and its current cash allocation. Some applications may therefore not be approved. If a grant is offered it may be subject to conditions such as a requirement that there be a specific timetable for completion of the project, for example within the financial year of the authority's cash allocation.

The FHSA or Health Board can offer any proportion between one third and two thirds of the actual cost of the approved work (including VAT) and the professional and planning fees of the project.

Eligibility of schemes

To be eligible for a grant, a project must be estimated to cost at least £800. This minimum amount is regularly updated by the Department of Health and the current figure is shown in the SFA. The figure is the cost of that part of the project which is eligible for a grant.

Eligible projects include:

• providing additional rooms, including a room for minor surgery, either by building or by bringing into practice use rooms not previously used;

- enlarging existing rooms;
- adding or improving lavatory facilities, washing facilities, lighting, ventilation and heating systems;
- extending telephone facilities within the surgery, other than for a trainee when the cost is reimbursable under the Trainee Practitioner Scheme;
- providing car and pram parking accommodation;
- double glazing;
- installing security systems; and
- carrying out work required by statute for fire precautions.

To gain approval the work must significantly improve the practice's services. Authorities will bear in mind the standards of accommodation considered in Chapter 16.

The proposed work must improve an existing structure, and cannot result in the provision of new premises. Thus grants are normally payable only for improvements to existing NHS practice premises which already have consulting and waiting rooms and have been accepted under the Rent and Rates Scheme. Premises which have not previously been used for practice purposes may be eligible for a grant if, in the view of the authority following an inspection, they are capable of being used as practice premises in their existing state. Where grants are paid for improving premises not previously used by doctors, there is a maximum grant payable. This is currently £7,300 per doctor, with an overall maximum of £25,500 per practice. These figures are regularly updated by SFA amendment.

Practices must have adequate security of tenure of the premises. If premises are not owned by the practice they must be held on a lease with an unexpired portion at least as long as the period of guaranteed use. In such cases the landlord's written consent must accompany the application.

Grants will only be paid for work relating specifically to NHS practice accommodation. If the work relates to shared accommodation, only a proportion of the cost will be acceptable for a grant.

If a project involves extending existing premises, a grant is only payable if any separate building is attached to the main building by at least a covered passage way and if the total area of the accommodation in the completed project does not exceed that shown in the Cost Rent Scheme maximum cost limits.

Ineligible schemes

Grants are not payable for the initial provision of premises, the cost of acquiring land or buildings, replacement or part replacement of premises, any work related to replacement of furniture (other than that built-in), furnishings, floor coverings or equipment, repair or maintenance work, restoration of structural damage, or any work in connection with non-practice accommodation. A project is also ineligible if the practice fails to obtain the prior approval of the FHSA or Health Board. The authority must be fully advised of proposals and of progress on the project.

Tax implications

If a practice applies for an improvement grant, it must declare at the end of that project that it does not intend to claim any tax relief on the cost of the work undertaken. Grants are not payable towards any expenses on which a tax allowance is being claimed, but if part of a project does not qualify for an improvement grant, tax relief can be claimed on that part of the work.

Practices should seek advice from their accountant as to whether it would be more favourable to claim tax relief or an improvement grant where this alternative is available.

It is most unusual for tax relief to be available on items for which an improvement grant may be given, because generally such grants are given for structural work rather than fixtures and fittings. In practice therefore there is often very little tax relief available, and so an improvement grant is advantageous.

If an item is eligible for either an improvement grant or tax relief, the improvement grant is for one third to two thirds of the cost of the item, whereas tax relief is given at the rate of 25% per annum on a reducing balance basis. As one is therefore comparing cash in hand of between 33% and 66% of the cost with tax relief at 40% on 25% of the cost, it is fair to say that as a general rule the improvement grant is more advantageous.

Guarantees of use

When an improvement grant is approved, the FHSA or Health Board will arrange for a contract to be signed by the parties. The contract will contain a declaration by the practice that the accommodation will remain in use for NHS purposes for a specified period of time. Currently for grants on projects costing up to £21,800 the premises must remain in use for three years, while for more costly projects use for four years is required. Changes to those provisions are shown in the SFA. If a practice fails to adhere to this declaration of guaranteed use, the FHSA or Health Board may require a repayment of the due proportion of the grant.

Method of application

A practice must obtain an application form (IG1) to apply for an improvement grant. The form asks for information about the practice and the proposed work, and an estimate of the costs. The application should indicate the proportion of the grant for which application is made.

Form IG1 should be returned to the FHSA or Health Board with a sketch plan of the premises as they are at present and a sketch plan of the proposed work, together with a schedule or specification of the work to be done and the proposed timetable.

If the cost of the project is over £7,300 (or such updated sum as is shown in the SFA), the drawings must be produced by an architect, surveyor or other suitably qualified person.

The practice will need to obtain any necessary planning consent from the local authority.

Quotations

Following the granting of approval by the FHSA or Health Board, the practice should obtain three competitive quotations for the work. Payment will be based upon the lowest of these, but it will be for the practice to choose whether it wishes to accept the lowest quotation. Having received the competitive quotations, the FHSA or Health Board will issue the agreement contract (form IG2), which must be signed by all members of the practice and by or on behalf of the General Manager of the authority.

Payment by instalments

If a project costs in excess of £7,300 (or the current appropriate amount), the FHSA or Health Board may be prepared to pay the grant to the practice by instalments, if so requested at the time of application. Before any instalments can be paid, the authority must be given certificates, signed by the architect, stating the total cost so far incurred on approved work.

Payments of instalments can be made until 90% of the estimated total grant is reached. The balance will not be paid until all the final documentation has been received.

Final payment

Once the work is finally completed and all the payments have been made by the practice, the claim for payment of the grant is made on form IG3. This form should be submitted, accompanied by all receipted bills and accounts, and must give the actual cost of any previously identified ineligible items. The claim form will need to be signed by the architect, in the case of a larger project, to certify that the work has been completed. The authority will then be in a position to pay the balance of the grant.

The effect on cost rent reimbursements

Although a practice has been approved to receive a cost rent reimbursement for substantial modifications to existing premises, this does not preclude it from also applying for an improvement grant. Not all the work eligible for cost rent payments is eligible for an improvement grant, and vice versa. Where an improvement grant is paid towards a cost rent project, the amount of the grant paid is deducted in the calculation of the cost rent reimbursement.

General guide to eligibility

Whilst individual authorities will have their own policies on what is eligible for an improvement grant, Box 17.1 gives a general guide to items which are normally eligible under the scheme. It is advisable to seek clarification of the local view on eligible items.

Box 17.1: Improvement Grant Scheme: Eligibility

	Eligible	*Ineligible*
1 Professional fees	a) architects b) quality surveyors c) building design consultants	a) solicitors b) accountants c) cost of any previous abortive work
2 Heating	a) Central heating to replace other forms of heating (i.e. electric, gas or open fires)	
3 Furniture	a) built-in waiting room seating b) built-in work benches, cupboards and filing systems (all constructed in situ and not just fixed to the structure)	a) all other items
4 Furnishings and floor coverings	a) carpets, carpeting and carpet tiles forming the floor of a newly constructed extension or in rooms structurally altered – must be fully fitted and permanently fixed b) curtains and rails around examination couches	a) window curtains b) pelmets and rails c) blinds d) rugs e) carpets, carpeting and carpet tiles (unless forming the floor of a newly constructed extension or in rooms structurally altered) or loose fitting floor covering

		Eligible	*Ineligible*
5	Equipment	No items eligible	Includes: a) radio telephones b) incinerators c) refrigerators d) sterilizers e) dictaphones and typewriters
6	Electrical and lighting systems	a) replacement of ordinary lighting systems by fluorescent fittings b) wall or anglepoise lights over examination couches c) additional power and lighting points	a) desk and table lamps b) rewiring of premises and rearrangement of circuits
7	Telephones	a) reasonable extensions to the telephone system	a) rental b) provision of extensions to the residential part of the premises and external extensions to doctors' residences
8	External works	a) pram porch b) car park	a) garages b) car ports c) work to gardens, fences, boundary walls and paths (unless directly associated with a new extension, entrance or exit)

	Eligible	Ineligible
9 Building work	a) double glazing for sound proofing purposes b) security systems c) fire precaution equipment as required by statute	a) repair or maintenance of premises, furniture, furnishings, floor coverings and equipment b) insulation
10 Miscellaneous		a) any project where a contract has been entered into, or work commenced, **without prior approval** of the authority

18 Applying for the Final Cost Rent

IMAGINE the project is now complete and the brand new surgery is ready for occupation. Many bills have been paid, an enormous overdraft hangs over the practice and the bank manager needs soothing. How does the practice get some money from the FHSA or Health Board?

Documentation

The practice must send to the authority receipted accounts for all work carried out. That is not necessarily as onerous as it sounds. Provided most work has been completed within the main contract with the builder, the practice will have been issued with interim certificates by the architect, and having paid those amounts will have received receipts. These interim certificates can be gathered together along with architect's accounts, legal accounts, bills for other items such as telephone systems (if appropriate) and, indeed, any accounts relating to professional fees or fixtures and fittings. A statement should be obtained from the bank showing the total amount of interest that has accrued on the special building account over the period of the building project, up to the operative date for cost rent reimbursement. There will of course be a retention fee which will not be paid to the builder until at least six months after completion.

The FHSA or Health Board will not expect the practice to wait until all bills have been paid and will be prepared to calculate an interim payment so as to ease the financial burden. When the final bills have been paid and submitted the authority will calculate the final figure and make any necessary retrospective adjustments.

Action by the FHSA or Health Board

Once the FHSA or Health Board has been told the new premises are in use and has received the receipted accounts, it will calculate a reimbursement based on what has been paid up to that time. The payment will become effective from the date shown on the architect's certificate of completion or the date on which the doctor moved into the premises, whichever is the later. Before making any payments, however, the authority may wish to arrange a formal inspection of the premises by officers or by a team.

In making payments, the authority will be able to make monthly advances; if this is not done automatically, a request should see it put into effect.

Final payments

When the final account has been issued and paid, the practice must submit any remaining receipted accounts to the authority. On receiving these, the FHSA or Health Board will examine the final account document and compare this to the original specification. This is done to ensure that major changes have not been made without approval.

The receipted accounts, the appropriate maximum cost limits and the assessments obtained from the District Valuer will be utilized to calculate a final cost rent reimbursement. The practice will be advised of the amount and method of calculation and payments will be made on that basis, with retrospective adjustments back to the date of occupation if necessary.

Method of calculation

Within the SFA there are 13 variations of Cost Rent Schemes. Five are straightforward: new premises, either owned or rented; substantial modification of existing premises; or those bought for alteration whether or not they are owned by the practice. The remaining eight varieties are for buildings which are owned by a bank and leased to the practice. The following schedule shows the method used to calculate each type of cost rent reimbursement.

If a site is leasehold, the FHSA or Health Board should be told at the time of initial application and provided, on seeing the lease, that it accepts the ground rent payable, it will reimburse the ground rent subject to apportionment by the District Valuer if there is a mix of practice and non-practice accommodation in the building scheme.

Cost rent calculations

New premises to be owned by the practice

The final cost rent to be reimbursed will be calculated as the prescribed percentage of the aggregate of:

1 the actual cost of the site at the date of acquisition by the practice or its current market value at the date of assessment by the District Valuer, whichever is the less;
2 fees and legal costs arising from the purchase of the site including the legal costs of obtaining a loan;
3 the cost, based on the lowest acceptable tender, of the building work, (including professional fees) or the notional cost for this work based on the appropriate maximum cost limits, whichever is the less;
4 where, before the completion of the building, loans are obtained to buy the site or to finance progress payments (to the maximum value of work done as certified by the architect), the interest charged on these loans up to the operative date of the cost rent reimbursement.

New premises rented from a third party

The final cost rent will be whichever is the less of the actual rent;

or

the prescribed percentage, at the date the new revised lease is signed, of:

1 the District Valuer's assessment of the value of the site at the date of assessment; plus
2 the maximum cost limit appropriate to the premises at the date the lease was signed; plus
3 the legal cost of the lease.

Premises bought for substantial modification

The final cost rent will be the prescribed percentage of the aggregate of *either*:

1 the actual cost of the site and premises at the date of acquisition by the practice, or their current market value at the date of assessment by the District Valuer, whichever is the less; *plus*
2 the cost, based on the lowest tender of the building work (including actual professional fees);

or

3 the current market value of the site (excluding the premises on it); *and*
4 the maximum cost limit appropriate to the premises at the date the tender for the building work was accepted;

whichever is the less; plus

5 fees and legal costs arising from the purchase of the site and premises, including the legal costs of obtaining a loan; and
6 where, before the completion of the work, loans are obtained to buy the site (and premises) and to finance progress payments (to the maximum value of work done as certified by the architect), the interest charged on these loans up to the operative date of the cost rent reimbursement.

Substantial modification of existing premises owned by the practice

The final cost rent will be *either*:

1 a combination of the reassessed current market rent or the existing cost rent (if any) of the original premises, whichever is the larger, and a cost rent calculated as the prescribed percentage of the aggregate of:

- the cost of the adaptation (including actual professional fees) and the cost of any additional land acquired by the practice or its value as assessed by the District Valuer, whichever is the less;
- the statutory cost of passing plans and first inspection of the building;
- fees and legal costs arising from the purchase of the additional land including, where applicable, the legal costs of obtaining a loan; and
- where, before completion of the adaptation, loans are obtained to buy additional land or finance progress payments (to the maximum value of the work done as certified by the architect), the interest charged on these loans up to the operative date of the final cost rent reimbursement.

or

2 the prescribed percentage of the aggregate of:

- the value of the site at the date of acquisition by the practice as assessed by the District Valuer plus whichever is the less of the value of any additional land similarly assessed or its actual cost;
- the maximum cost limit for new purpose-built premises of the same size as the accommodation when completed;
- fees and legal costs arising from the purchase of the additional land including, where applicable, the legal costs of obtaining a loan; and
- where, before completion of the adaptation, loans are obtained to buy additional land or finance progress payments (to the maximum value of the work done as certified by the architect), the interest charged on these loans up to the operative date of the final cost rent reimbursement;

whichever is the less.

Substantial modification of existing premises not owned by the practice

The final cost rent will be whichever is the less of the actual rent;

or

the prescribed percentage (at the date the new or revised lease is signed) of:

1 the District Valuer's assessment of the value of the site as at the date of the last revision of the rental of the existing premises before modification; plus
2 the maximum cost limit appropriate to the premises as modified at the date the new or revised lease was signed; plus
3 the legal costs of the lease.

New premises to be purchased by a bank on completion

The final cost rent will be whichever is the less of the actual rent;

or

the prescribed percentage of the aggregate of:

1 the actual cost of the site at the date of acquisition by the practice or its current market value at the date of assessment by the District Valuer, whichever is the less;
2 the cost, based on the lowest acceptable tender, of the building work (including professional fees) plus the statutory cost of passing plans and first inspection of the building or the notional cost for the building work based on the appropriate maximum cost limits (which includes the statutory cost of passing plans and first inspection of building), whichever is the less;
3 fees and legal costs arising from the purchase of the site including, where applicable, legal costs of obtaining a loan;
4 where, before completion of the premises, loans are obtained to buy the site or to finance progress payments (to the maximum value of the work done as certified by the architect), the interest charged on these loans up to the operative date of the final cost rent reimbursement;
5 professional and legal expenses of the group and the bank necessarily and reasonably incurred in connection with the bank's acquisition of the premises and the granting of the lease, in so far as they are taken into account by the bank in the calculation of the rent charged to the group.

(In the eight schemes detailed on pages 128 to 137, 'group' normally means a practice of two or more doctors.)

Premises bought by the practice for substantial alteration to be purchased by a bank on completion

The final cost rent will be whichever is the less of the actual rent;

or

the prescribed percentage of the aggregate of *either*:

1 the actual cost of the site and premises at the date of acquisition by the practice, or their current market value at the date of assessment by the District Valuer, whichever is the less; plus
2 the cost, based on the lowest acceptable tender, of the building work (including professional fees); plus
3 the statutory cost of passing plans and first inspection of the building;

or

4 the current market value of the site (excluding the premises on it) as assessed by the District Valuer; plus
5 the maximum cost limit appropriate to the premises (which includes the statutory cost of passing plans and first inspection of the building) at the date the practitioner signs the lease;

whichever is the less;

6 plus fees and legal costs arising from the purchase of the site and premises, including where applicable the legal costs of obtaining a loan;
7 where, before the completion of the work, loans are obtained to buy the site and premises and to finance progress payments (to the maximum value of work done as certified by the architect), the interest charged on these loans up to the operative date of the final cost rent reimbursement; and
8 professional and legal expenses of the group and the bank necessarily incurred in connection with the bank's acquisition of the premises and the granting of the lease, in so far as they are taken into account by the bank in the calculation of the rent charged to the group.

Substantial alteration of existing practice premises to be purchased by a bank on completion

The final cost rent will be whichever is the less of the actual rent;

or

a rent calculated as *either*:

1 the reassessed current market rent or the existing cost rent (if any) of the original premises, whichever is the larger; plus
2 a cost rent calculated as the prescribed percentage of:

- the cost of the adaptation (including actual professional fees) and the cost of any additional land acquired by the practice or its value assessed by the District Valuer, whichever is the less;
- the statutory cost of passing plans and first inspection of the building;
- where, before completion of the premises, loans are obtained to buy additional land or finance progress payments (to the maximum value of the work done as certified by the architect), the interest charged on these loans up to the operative date of the final cost rent reimbursement;
- professional and legal expenses of the group and the bank necessarily incurred in connection with the bank's acquisition of the premises and the granting of the lease, in so far as they are taken into account by the bank in the calculation of the rent charged to the group;

or

3 the prescribed percentage of:

- the value of the site at the date of acquisition by the practice as assessed by the District Valuer plus whichever is the less of the value of any additional land similarly assessed or its actual cost; plus
- the maximum cost limit for new purpose-built premises of the same size as the existing premises after completion (which includes the statutory cost of passing plans and first inspection of the building) at the date the practitioners sign the lease; plus
- where, before completion of the adaptation, loans are obtained to buy additional land or finance progress payments (to the maximum value of the work done as certified by the architect), the interest charged on these loans up to the operative date of the final cost rent reimbursement;

- professional and legal expenses of the group and the bank necessarily and reasonably incurred in connection with the bank's acquisition of the premises and the granting of the lease, in so far as they are taken into account by the bank in the calculation of the rent charged to the group;

whichever is the less.

Site purchased by a bank from a third party

In the case of a site purchased by a bank from a third party on which new premises are then erected by the practice, the final cost rent will be whichever is the less of the actual rent;

or

the prescribed percentage of the aggregate of:

1 the current market value of the site at the date of assessment by the District Valuer;
2 the cost, based on the lowest acceptable tender, of the building work (including professional fees) plus the statutory cost of passing plans and first inspection of the building or the notional cost for this work based on the appropriate maximum cost limits at the date the practitioners sign the lease (which includes the statutory cost of passing plans and first inspection of the building), whichever is the less;
3 where before completion of the premises loans are obtained to finance progress payments (to the maximum value of the work done as certified by the architect), the interest charged on these loans up to the operative date of the final cost rent reimbursement and site licence fees paid under the Building Agreement;
4 professional and legal expenses of the group and the bank necessarily and reasonably incurred in connection with the bank's acquisition of the site and premises, the Building Agreement and the grant of the lease in so far as they are taken into account by the bank in the calculation of the rent charged to the group.

Premises purchased by a bank from a third party

In the case of premises purchased by a bank from a third party which are then substantially altered by the practice the final cost rent will be whichever is the less of the actual rent;

or

the prescribed percentage of the aggregate of *either*:

1 the current market value of the site and premises at the date of assessment by the District Valuer;
2 the cost based on the lowest tender, of the building work (including actual professional fees);
3 the statutory cost of passing plans and first inspection of the building;

or

4 the current market value of the site (excluding the premises on it) as assessed by the District Valuer; plus
5 the maximum cost limit appropriate to the premises at the date the practitioner signs the lease (which includes the statutory cost of passing plans and first inspection of the building);

whichever is the less; plus

6 where before completion of the work loans are obtained to finance progress payments (to the maximum value of work done as certified by the architect), the interest charged on these loans up to the operative date of the final cost rent reimbursement and site licence fees paid under the Building Agreement;
7 professional and legal expenses of the group and the bank necessarily incurred in connection with the bank's acquisition of the premises, the Building Agreement and the grant of the lease in so far as they are taken into account by the bank in the calculation of the rent charged to the group.

Site owned by the practice and purchased by a bank prior to erection of the premises

In the case of a site already owned by the practice prior to sale to a bank the final cost rent will be whichever is the less of the actual rent;

or

the prescribed percentage on the date the practitioners sign the lease of the aggregate of:

1 the actual cost of the site at the date of acquisition by the practice or its current market value at that date as assessed by the District Valuer, whichever is the less;
2 the cost, based on the lowest acceptable tender of the building work (including professional fees) plus the statutory cost of passing plans and first inspection of the building or the notional cost for the building work based on the appropriate maximum cost limits at the date the practitioners sign the lease (which includes the statutory cost of passing plans and first inspection of building), whichever is the less;
3 where before completion of the premises loans are obtained to finance progress payments (to the maximum value of the work done as certified by the architect), the interest charged on these loans up to the operative date of the final cost rent reimbursement and the site licence fee paid under the Building Agreement;
4 professional and legal expenses of the group and the bank necessarily and reasonably incurred in connection with the bank acquisition of the site, the Building Agreement and the grant of the lease, in so far as they are taken into account by the bank in the rent charged to the group.

Existing practice premises owned by the practice and purchased by a bank prior to substantial adaptation

The final cost rent will be whichever is the less of the actual rent;

or

a rent calculated as *either*:

1 the reassessed current market rent or the existing cost rent (if any) of the original premises, whichever is the larger; plus
2 a cost rent calculated as the prescribed percentage on the date the practitioners sign the lease of:

- the cost of the adaptation (including actual professional fees) and the cost of any additional land acquired by the practice or its value as assessed by the District Valuer, whichever is the less;
- the statutory cost of passing loans and first inspection of the building;
- where, before completion of the premises, loans are obtained to finance progress payments (to the maximum value of the work done as certified by the architect), the interest charged on the loan up to the operative date of the final cost rent reimbursement and site licence fee paid under the Building Agreement (net of any current market or cost rent reimbursement paid to the group in respect of the premises during the period of the Building Agreement);
- professional and legal expenses of the group and the bank necessarily incurred in connection with the bank's acquisition of the premises prior to adaptation, the Building Agreement and the grant of the lease, in so far as they are taken into account by the bank in the rent charged to the group;

or

3 the prescribed percentage of:

- the value of the site at the date of acquisition by the practice as assessed by the District Valuer plus whichever is the less of the value of any additional land similarly assessed or its actual cost; plus
- the appropriate maximum cost limit for new purpose-built premises of the same size as the existing premises after adaptation (which includes the statutory cost of passing plans and first inspection of the building) at the date the practitioners sign the lease; plus

- where, before completion of the adaptation, loans are obtained to finance progress payments (to the maximum value of the work done as certified by the architect), the interest charged on these loans up to the operative date of the final cost rent reimbursement and site licence fee paid under the Building Agreement (net of any current market rent or cost rent reimbursement paid to the group in respect of the premises during the period of the Building Agreement); plus
- professional and legal expenses of the group and the Bank necessarily and reasonably incurred in connection with the bank acquisition of the premises prior to adaptation, the Building Agreement and the grant of the lease, in so far as they are taken into account by the bank in the rent charged to the group;

whichever is the less.

Newly constructed or adapted premises acquired by a bank from a third party

In the case of new premises, the final cost rent will be whichever is the less of the actual rent;

or

the prescribed percentage on the date the practitioners sign the lease of the aggregate of:

1 the District Valuer's assessment of the value of the site at the date of assessment; plus
2 the maximum cost limit appropriate to the premises at the date the lease is signed; plus
3 professional and legal expenses of the group and the bank necessarily and reasonably incurred in connection with the bank's acquisition of the premises and the granting of the lease, in so far as they are taken into account by the bank in the calculation of the rent charged to the group.

In the case of adapted premises not previously used as surgery premises by the group the final cost rent will be determined as in the above, the District Valuer's valuation being for the site only and excluding the premises on it and the schedule cost being that applicable to the premises as adapted.

In the case of practice premises already rented by the group from a third party and purchased by the bank following substantial adaptation by the third party, the final cost rent will be whichever is the less of the actual rent;

or

the prescribed percentage on the date the practitioners sign the lease of:

1 the District Valuer's assessment of the value of the site as at the date of the last revision of the rental of the existing premises before modification; plus
2 the maximum cost limit appropriate to the premises as modified at the date the lease with the bank is signed; plus
3 professional and legal expenses of the group and the bank necessarily and reasonably incurred in connection with the acquisition of the premises and the granting of the lease, in so far as they are taken into account by the bank in the calculation of the rent charged to the group.

Right of appeal

Where a practice is dissatisfied with the District Valuer's assessment of the current market value of either the site, or the premises acquired for conversion, it can submit to the FHSA or Health Board a statement with reasons for disagreeing with the valuation. This will be considered by the DV, who may discuss the valuation either with the practice or its professional advisers. The DV may initiate a discussion when he or she considers that this would help remove any misunderstandings.

A doctor can make representations to the Secretary of State if he or she remains dissatisfied with:

- the assessment of the current market value of the site, or of premises acquired for conversion;
- a decision of the FHSA or Health Board that a project will not produce premises complying with the recommended standards; or
- the final cost rent as determined by the authority.

In any such event, representations must be submitted to the Secretary of State within two months of the date of the authority's final decision and should include, or be followed as soon as possible by, a statement of reasons. The right of appeal is embodied in the Statement of Fees and Allowances, which should be referred to in any letter making representations.

Cost rents in Scotland

The Cost Rent Scheme for doctors in Scotland is virtually the same as in England and Wales, but contact with the local Health Board will elicit any particular point of detail which may be relevant.

19 The Roles of the Constituents

The Family Health Services Authority or Health Board

Acceptance of premises

As a doctor's terms of service set down the basic requirements for the provision of surgery premises and the SFA sets out ways of encouraging the improvement of them when necessary, the authority can have both a 'stick and carrot' approach. Premises must be approved under the terms of service, although such approval does not automatically imply rent or rates reimbursements will be made.

If authorities take the view that, for instance, branch surgeries are being provided speculatively without a justified service need, or the cost of upgrading a surgery is not warranted, rent and rates reimbursement can be either withheld or maintained at the level appropriate to the original state of the accommodation.

Authorities may have their own policy for branch surgery provision to prevent unnecessary proliferation, so early discussion is vital if a practice is considering such a venture.

Approval of cost rents

It is the FHSA or Health Board which approves cost rent projects. Without such approval projects will be very expensive for their initiators, as there will be no reimbursement of the cost-related expenditure.

In giving its approval the authority will review the standard of the existing accommodation and the proposals for improving it. It will look at the service provision and objectives of the practice and will expect to see it planning for the future.

With a cash limit which includes cost rent reimbursements, the authority will look carefully at the likely cost of a project in terms of the reimbursement it will generate, and it will have to make a decision as to when a particular project will fit into its plans for the overall improvement of surgeries throughout the area. Proposals will be prioritized and doctors advised when the money may be available for a cost rent reimbursement.

In addition, the authority will look closely at the design of the new building, or alterations to existing premises, to ensure that the criteria for new purpose-built surgery premises are being fulfilled through the provision of a functional building with the appropriate levels of confidentiality and privacy for patients at reception counters and during consultations.

Free advice

The authority is always available to give free advice at all stages of a cost rent project. Admittedly, it cannot undertake work properly within the province of the professionals involved, but the experience of its officers will enable it to give guidance about what to do and what not to do.

Payments

Perhaps the authority's most important role is that of paymaster for rent, rates and cost rent reimbursements and improvement grants.

The District Valuer

Advice to the FHSA or Health Board

The District Valuer acts as the authority's agent by carrying out assessments and reviews of current market rent, and valuations of sites and premises. In performing these functions he or she must work within the constraints of the Rent and Rates Scheme and cannot carry out ad hoc valuations or give advice directly to the practice.

Current market rent

The current market rent is the amount which the District Valuer considers might reasonably be paid for the premises on the date of the valuation. The District Valuer's basis of calculation used in assessing current market rent will differ between owner-occupied premises and rented premises, but in both cases the aim will be to arrive at a rent which can be agreed with the doctors (or their representative) before his or her report is made to the authority.

The method used by the District Valuer in making his or her assessment in the various circumstances is as follows:

- where the practice accommodation forms part of an owner-occupied residence, the current market rent will be assessed as a part of the whole premises, and not increased or reduced to reflect any advantage there may be in the fact that the practice accommodation is not in separate premises;
- where the practice accommodation forms part of an owner-occupied residence and includes part which is used regularly but not exclusively for practice purposes, the current market rent will be assessed similarly and an agreed percentage added of the current market rental value of that part of the premises used regularly but not exclusively for practice purposes; and
- where the practice accommodation forms part of a residence owned or rented by a person not connected with the practice, the current market rent will be assessed for the practice accommodation only, and will not reflect any advantage or disadvantage there may be in the fact that this is not in separate premises.

Reaching agreement

The District Valuer will normally be open to negotiation with either the practice or its adviser on any assessments of current market rent or valuations of site or premises. The District Valuer's aim is to reach agreement before reporting to the authority, but if agreement cannot be reached, the FHSA or Health Board is obliged to notify the practice of that valuation. If the practice is aggrieved, it has the right to make representations to the Secretary of State.

Section 5

20 Pitfalls: An FHSA General
       Manager's View

Sites

SITES can be difficult to find. A site which is in a good position may be
so commercially attractive to a developer that the practice cannot match
the price being offered. Nevertheless, finding a site in the right location
to meet the needs of the practice's patients is of paramount importance
and detailed research into the distribution of patients is critical, as are
discussions with the authority, which will need to be convinced that any
particular location is the right one before giving the go ahead.

- When looking for a site, doctors should alway consult the local
  planning authority (the borough, district or county council) and
  health authorities, to see if they have any sites lying dormant. It is
  surprising how often a council or health authority has land which can
  be made available for a surgery development.
- To ensure that the price of a site fairly reflects its market value,
  doctors should let the authority know the relevant details so that an
  informal report from the District Valuer can be sought and an
  estimated cost rent provided, from which a deduction can then be
  made of the District Valuer's view of the site's value.
- Doctors should be aware of hidden costs. As suggested earlier, good
  sites are often bought eagerly by developers. It is not uncommon for
  doctors to have to settle for poorer sites with problems which cause
  building difficulties and extra costs. Hidden mine shafts, sewers,
  service cables or gas pipes crossing sites are not uncommon. In the
  past, authorities have been able to include justified additional costs
  within the cost rent reimbursement as exceptional site costs, but with
  cash limits such flexibility may be severely curtailed. If exceptional
  site costs are expected, or come to notice late, authorities may expect
  the practice to negotiate a reduced site cost with the vendor.
- Sites which have covenants upon them should be avoided whenever
  possible. Removal of such covenants can be expensive and time-
  consuming.
- Acquiring the chosen site can be a lengthy process and there are no
  hard and fast rules about whether private or public vendors are the

slowest. Doctors should be patient and plan the development well in advance.

Planning authorities

Increasingly, planning authorities are tending to impose some conditions upon the building of new surgery premises or extensions to existing buildings. For example, a practice in a building which has existed in a town area for many years with minimal parking may find that, to build an extension, it will be required to provide off-street parking spaces.

The key to avoiding the imposition of unexpected conditions is to talk informally to officers of the planning authority at a very early stage. Whilst officers' views are not always reflected by the planning committee, an indication of the likely outcome will be given.

In the past planning authorities may have tended to add conditions to planning constraints when cost rent projects were not cash limited. In the future, with cash constraints, FHSAs, and Health Boards may be reluctant to accept such conditions as exceptional site costs.

Professional advisers

While doctors may feel that they need the expertise of professional advisers when undertaking a cost rent project, they should remember that these cost non-reimbursable money. Advisers can be useful in removing a great deal of the workload from the practice's shoulders. In a large practice one member may take the lead role for the project, but as this can involve a great deal of time it is necessary to weigh up whether that time could be better spent if a professional adviser were employed. It should be remembered of course that the FHSA or Health Board is always available for free advice.

Architects

Architects' expertise in dealing with doctors' surgeries and the Cost Rent Scheme varies considerably. GPs should look at other surgeries and talk to the doctors concerned about their experiences before selecting an architect. It is very important to remember to tell the architect what the practice wants. He or she has the professional expertise to give guidance on what is and what is not possible, but doctors should ensure that the architect does not run away with the project. Architects may present desirable proposals as if they are necessary, and those proposals may be very expensive. At the end of the day it is the practice which has to finance the project and has to fund any overspending itself. The practice should ensure that the architect's plans enable the surgery to be expanded easily at a later date.

Planning for the future

It always helps to plan well ahead. Doctors should not build premises which are too small. A practice may only ever undertake one cost rent project and it would be disappointing, frustrating and expensive if within a short time there is not enough space.

Always talk to the FHSA or Health Board and to local councils about projected population changes. The FHSA or Health Board will be able to say when it is likely to approve an additional partner for instance, and if that day is not too far away it may well agree to additional space for a further partner in advance of any appointment.

If a practice is likely to become a training practice in the future and a member of the practice is to undertake training for this, the plans should incorporate a trainee suite. If the practice is not yet computerized, enough office space, and preferably a separate area, should be provided for probable computerization in the future.

Finance

It pays to shop around for finance because there are numerous banks and other financial institutions willing to lend money for cost rent projects.

It is important to open a dedicated bank account from which all money will be paid for the project. Doctors should have an agreement with the lender that they will not have to repay any of the loan until the cost rent reimbursement has started once the project is complete. By rolling up the interest on this account, the amount of interest can easily be identified, and added to the cost rent reimbursement. If doctors do not keep the finances for the building separate from other practice expenses, it will be difficult to identify interest relating specifically to the building work, and the practice may lose out.

Architect or builder bankruptcy

If the architect or builder becomes bankrupt there will be many problems. If the builder goes bankrupt, the architect should be able to find a new builder to complete the project. The FHSA or Health Board should be informed, and may be sympathetic if the final costs are above those orginally expected.

The bankruptcy of an architect can be a greater problem because it can be difficult to find another architect willing to step in and sign completion certificates without carrying out a major review of what has gone on before, and consequently charging a high fee. Again, the FHSA or Health Board should be contacted for advice.

21 Changing to Current Market Rent

Triennial reviews

THE cost rent reimbursement for new or modified premises is an alternative to receiving a current market rent. The practice will, however, initially be eligible to receive whichever amount is the higher, but cannot revert to cost rent from current market rent. At the start it is extremely unlikely that a current market rent would be greater than a cost rent, although this has been known to occur in parts of Central London. The practice should not normally therefore request the FHSA or Health Board to review the current market rent at the date the cost rent comes into effect, unless there are good reasons to believe that the current market rent will exceed the cost rent. Once a cost rent reimbursement has started it will continue until the practice chooses, following a triennial review, to change to a current market rental or until the premises (or a significant part of them) cease to be used for practice purposes.

As with premises receiving notional rents, the authority will arrange for the current market rent of cost rented premises owned by a practice to be reviewed three years from the date on which they were first brought into use, and triennially thereafter. Form PREM1 will be required and the District Valuer will be asked to assess the current market rental of the premises. When this is reported to the practice, it will have the opportunity to seek professional advice and elect to change to the current market rent if that course is more favourable. Normally it takes several triennial reviews before a change to a current market rent reimbursement is advantageous, but the time depends on the size of the project, the location of the practice and the financial climate.

Leased premises

Where premises are leased by a practice, it will receive reimbursement which is the lesser of the actual rent paid or the cost rent calculation on the maximum cost limit. When a review of the rent payable is due under the terms of the lease, or a new lease is entered into at the end of the full term of the existing lease, the practice can seek a review by submitting forms PREM1. The District Valuer will be asked to assess whether the revised rental payable is reasonable.

Where premises have been modified, reviews of current market rent will relate to the whole of the new premises. There is no reassessment of the current market rent figure of the original building which was used for the cost rent calculation.

When to change to current market rent

A practice will opt for a current market rent when it exceeds the cost rent reimbursement. The only possible exception occurs if the practice is receiving a cost rent reimbursement based on a variable interest rate at a time when interest rates are rising rapidly. In such circumstances, if a current market rent is only marginally greater than the cost rent, the practice may wish to remain with cost rent reimbursement, accepting a short-term loss on the assumption that interest rate rises will result in an increase in the prescribed percentage, which may in turn increase the cost rent reimbursement above the current market rental figure. This is a gamble!

22 Partnership Agreements

THIS chapter is concerned with how practice premises should be addressed in a partnership agreement, rather than the wider issues concerning partnership deeds. Whether the agreement is being drawn up de novo or whether it is being revised to accommodate the new circumstances of property ownership, it should be drafted by the practice solicitor. The practice accountant, the Local Medical Committee secretary and the BMA's industrial relations officers are also sources of important advice.

Basis of occupation

The partnership deed should specify the basis of occupation of all the premises used by the practice. In other words, the premises should be listed, and the agreement should state whether the premises are owned, leased or held on a licence.

Capital assets and partnership capital

The deed should identify the capital assets used by the practice, and the arrangements whereby incoming partners acquire appropriate shares in those assets. The capital of a medical partnership may have up to three components: property; other fixed asset capital, such as fixtures and fittings, furniture, office equipment and medical and surgical equipment; and working capital, including such items as drug stock, capital held in a bank or building society, and funds owed by debtors, less sums owed to creditors.

The agreement should also state what is comprised in the partnership capital. Where one or more of the existing partners own freehold or leasehold premises which are used by the partnership, the deed should clearly indicate whether the value of such interests is included in or excluded from the partnership capital. If the premises are owned by one or more partners, the deed should specify an agreed period of notice which will be given to the non-owning partner or partners by the owning partner or partners or their personal representatives, if they wish to acquire the practice premises for their own use.

Valuation

The agreement must specify details of how partnership assets are to be valued when partners join or leave the practice.

Possible alternative bases of valuation are discussed on pages 53 and 54. The parties concerned have to agree on a valuer: a deed might specify a particular firm of estates surveyors and valuers, or a firm recommended by the BMA, or a valuer nominated by the Royal Institution of Chartered Surveyors. The deed should indicate whether one valuation is to be binding on both parties – the retiring and remaining partners – and whether the same valuation is to be binding on an incoming partner or partners. If more than one valuation is to be obtained, the deed should indicate whether the parties concerned should agree the final valuation, or whether agreement should be reached by a specified method of arbitration. The agreement should also indicate who bears the costs of valuation and of any arbitration.

No valuation should include any sale or purchase of goodwill.

Because valuation can be technically difficult and expensive, some partnership deeds avoid a requirement for actual revaluation of the property and provide for valuation according to a predetermined formula, taking into account the original cost of the building, and the ratio between the current market rent, if higher than the cost rent, and the cost rent.

It is usual to include a clause to the effect that the valuation to be placed on the surgery would not at any time be less than the original development cost. Without such a clause, partners who retire early in the life of the premises, when the outstanding loan on the building is higher than the current valuation and there is in effect negative equity, would be disadvantaged. Some such clauses are rendered void when the partnership has elected to change from a cost rent to a current market rent.

Insurance policies

Some partnerships borrowing money for premises development by the endowment method treat the premiums on the relevant insurance policies as a practice expense. In these circumstances, the partnership agreement should specify how the policies are to be valued if one of the borrowers leaves the practice before the loan is repaid. The advice of the practice accountant should be sought when the deed is drafted.

Retirement

The partnership agreement should specify the arrangements for purchase of an outgoing partner's share in the premises. It is normal to require the remaining partners to purchase the share from the retiring partner, or the executors of a deceased partner, within a specified period. The deed should also provide for the payment of interest to the retiring partner or the estate of the deceased partner, to recompense for any delay in purchasing the share.

23 Taxation Issues

VAT

The necessity of registering for VAT under the self-supply regulations has been dealt with on pages 110 to 112. The provisions of the 1989 Finance Act mean that all property developers, including GPs, have to register for VAT purposes where the project was commenced on or after 1 August 1989 and has a total cost of more than £100,000. It is advisable to register at the outset of the development, else some VAT may not be recoverable. It is also sensible to register as a repayment trader to aid practice cash flow; VAT can then be reclaimed monthly rather than quarterly. Penalties will be incurred if a practice fails to apply for VAT registration. Notice 742A on property development, produced by HM Customs and Excise, gives useful information, and the practice accountant's advice should always be sought, particularly on the timing of deregistration.

VAT (Buildings and Land) Order 1991

This order introduces the concept of 'developmental leases'. A tenant developer is now obliged to notify the landlord if he or she becomes subject to a self-supply charge, normally on completion of the work. Thereafter, the landlord will be obliged to charge VAT at the standard rate on future rent.

The order also extends the self-supply provisions to the extension, enlargement or reconstruction of an existing building, if the construction or civil engineering work commenced on or after 1 January 1992.

Extensions (including annexes with internal access to the existing building) and enlargements are defined in the order as:

- being carried out wholly or partly on land (to be known as 'new building land') adjoining the curtilage of the existing building; or
- providing a total gross external floor area (excluding any floor area on new building land) which increases the total floor area of the original building by 20% or more; and
- having a total value of self-supply of not less than £100,000.

However, the extension, enlargement or civil engineering work will not be subject to the self-supply charge if the developer has held at least 75% of the relevant land interest for 10 years prior to the date the property, as modified, is put to an exempt use (such as the supply of services by a registered medical practitioner).

Reconstructions are defined in the order as works carried out on an existing building, in the course of which at least 80% of the floor structures of the original building are removed, whether or not they are subsequently replaced in whole or in part, for which the total value of the self-supply is not less than £100,000.

GPs may therefore be affected by the order in various circumstances. If a GP is a freeholder of an existing non-domestic building, and is enlarging, extending or reconstructing the building, either for his or her own use or for granting an exempt lease or licence to a tenant, registration for VAT will be required.

If a GP is a tenant or licensee, and is enlarging, extending or re-constructing the building, either for his or her own use or for granting exempt sub-leases to tenants, the GP will not only have to register for VAT, but also have to notify the landlord and pay VAT on future rent.

If a GP is a landlord, and has granted a developmental lease to a tenant, the tenant will have to notify the GP that he or she has become subject to a self-supply charge, and will thereafter have to pay VAT on rent.

Improvement grants

One condition of claiming an improvement grant is that a tax allowance cannot also be claimed on the same expenditure. Many improvements or alterations to the structure of a building do not attract capital allowances, but tax relief can be claimed on some improvements. GPs have to decide which of the two options is preferable, and should seek their accountant's advice. For most projects, it is beneficial to claim an improvement grant and forgo tax relief. Further information is given on page 115.

Furnishings and equipment

Where furnishings and equipment have been classified as fixtures and included in the building costs, it is helpful if the architect or builder can list these items together with their costs, so that capital allowances can be obtained where possible, at a rate of 25% per annum on a reducing balance basis. No tax relief can be claimed on the costs of the structure of the building.

Interest on loans

Interest on surgery loans is allowable in full for tax purposes, although only those partners owning shares in the surgery premises should obtain tax relief. Rolled up interest included in the principal of the loan is also fully allowable.

Practice accounts

Cost rent or current market rent paid to a GP when his or her privately owned surgery is used to see NHS patients, is not treated as rent for income tax purposes, but is assessable to Schedule D, Case II, as it is received by virtue of a GP's contract for services within the NHS. However, it may be allocated in different proportions to the trading profits, to reflect the ownership shares. Treatment by any other means could jeopardize claims for Capital Gains Tax retirement relief.

Because premises are often owned in ratios other than the standard profit-sharing ratios, and indeed because some partners may not own a share of the premises, it is particularly important that cost rent or notional rent and any other rentals received are credited to the surgery owners and not to the other partners, and that the costs of servicing any loan are similarly allotted. Such property transactions should be shown separately in the practice's annual accounts.

Netting out

As with other direct reimbursements, expenses on rent and rates should be shown in full in practice accounts, and payments under the rent and rates scheme should be shown as income. Otherwise the annual surveys of practice expenses carried out by the Inland Revenue will produce unreliable and erroneous data and the remuneration of all GPs will be artificially depressed.

Capital Gains Tax

Capital Gains Tax was introduced in 1965 in order to tax gains made through the disposal of capital assets. Currently, chargeable gains are taxed on an individual's top rate of tax, with an annual exemption of the first £5000 of any gain. The Capital Gains Tax retirement relief provisions mean there is little prospect of a Capital Gains Tax charge when a share of surgery premises is sold, so long as certain conditions are satisfied.

24 Avoiding the Pitfalls: A GP's View

This final chapter summarizes some of the important advice that has been given earlier in the book, in the form of a checklist of issues which need to be addressed by any practice embarking on a cost rent scheme.

Preliminary

- One member of the practice should have principal responsibility for overseeing the cost rent scheme, and should be allowed sufficient time for that responsibility.
- At least one partner should be fully conversant with paragraph 51 of the Statement of Fees and Allowances.
- The advice of the FHSA or Health Board should be sought at the earliest stage.
- The practice accountant and an architect should be involved at an early stage.
- Ideas for premises design should be sought through visits to other surgeries.
- Advice should be sought from other doctors with cost rent schemes in progress or recently completed.

Options

- All possible options for premises development should be considered, including an improvement grant scheme and, within the Cost Rent Scheme, alterations or extensions to the existing premises, alterations or extensions to other premises, or the construction of new premises.
- All factors affecting the choice of possible options should be considered, including size, cost, the future value of the premises (taking into account the expected life of the building and maintenance and running costs), location, ease of access, disruption (during construction or through moving), and planning consents.
- The current activities, operational policies and organization of the practice should be analysed.

- Activity sequences, in terms of the movements of primary health care team members and of the public, should be identified.
- The future needs of the practice, and possible future developments in primary care, should be considered and planned for.
- The premises design should be as flexible as possible, allowing:
  - the maintenance of efficient operation despite fluctuating workload
  - the optimization of space sharing and multiple use of space
  - general purpose clinical rooms
  - the provision of consultations, clinics, classes and group sessions
  - adaptation to shifting patterns of primary care.
- Space should be adequate for the range of services and the demand for services envisaged.
- The possible requirement for modifications or extensions to cope with future change should be considered.
- The views of doctors, staff and patients should be sought.
- Adequate time should be allowed for discussion and planning.

FHSA or Health Board

- Agreement in principle to the proposals for premises development (outline approval) should be sought at the outset.
- Advice should be sought about the authority's guidelines for the approval of projects with local priorities.
- The priority accorded to the project in the authority's forward programme for premises improvement should be ascertained.
- The financial year in which cost rent reimbursement can be anticipated should be ascertained.
- The FHSA or Health Board may need to be involved in representations to the local authority planning committee.
- The receipt of a formal offer in writing including an interim cost rent assures the project of financial support and allows the safe purchase of land or buildings.
- Any subsequent significant variation in design should be notified to the authority, so that a revised interim cost rent can be calculated.
- The authority should be consulted if doctors developing premises which they will own have difficulty obtaining three competitive tenders.

- The authority must be told if there is a risk of overrunning the target completion date.
- The authority's advice as to what fixtures and fittings are allowable within the scheme should be sought.

Premises design

- The building design must respect the requirement for confidentiality.
- Public, clinical and staff zones should be separate.
- Clinical facilities should preferably be on the ground floor.
- The common room should allow flexible use.
- The heating system should allow intermittent and variable operation because of the varying pattern of use of the premises during the day.
- The premises should be energy-efficient.
- A records storage system should be chosen.
- A telephone system, adequate for internal and external communication requirements, should be chosen.
- Adequate space should be provided for a practice computer system.
- Wireways or ducts suitable for a networked or multiuser computer system should be provided.
- The location of sinks, sockets and radiators should be determined.
- Suitable lighting for general illumination, and for illumination for patient examination and operative and other procedures, should be chosen.
- A treatment utility area should be provided.
- Adequate storage facilities, including space for the storage of supplies for practice and community nurses, clinical waste, and cleaners' supplies, should be provided.
- Fire fighting equipment and smoke detectors should be installed.
- Security alarms should be installed after the advice of the police crime prevention officer has been sought.
- The design specifications should preferably not be altered after a tender has been accepted.

Finance

- A capital budget for the project should be agreed with the practice accountant.

- Options for funding should be discussed with the practice accountant, and possibly with the FHSA or Health Board, the BMA Regional Office and other practices.
- The practice should not overcommit itself financially, but should ensure it can meet the commitments resulting from the project, including repayment of capital and running and maintenance costs, after allowing for cost rent reimbursement.
- The practice should be aware of those costs which are not allowable within the Cost Rent Scheme, including:
  - all costs in excess of the SFA schedule maximum in each category, except those approved in advance by the FHSA or Health Board
  - the cost of non-allowable items included in the project
  - the site cost in excess of the District Valuer's valuation.
- Compliance with the practice budget should be monitored.
- If the practice is contemplating employing a consultancy or developer to see the development through from inception to completion:
  - the advice of the FHSA or Health Board should be sought
  - the developer should be approached for the names of previous clients who can supply references
  - the possibility should be fully discussed with the practice accountant and solicitor before any contract is entered into.
- The practice should shop around, exploring many possible sources of finance.
- Factors which may influence the choice of a source of finance include not only the competitiveness of interest rates, but also the method of paying interest, and the flexibility, understanding of primary care and rapport with the practice of the lender.
- A repayment arrangement should be chosen which meets the needs of the partners.
- The practice should enquire whether differing interest rates and loan terms apply to Cost Rent Scheme overruns and additional fixtures and fittings.
- Provision should be made for short term or interim funding, in order to meet those costs falling due for payment prior to completion of the project.
- Advice should be taken from the practice accountant and from the FHSA or Health Board about the merits and disadvantages of fixed rate and variable rate loans.

- Full information should be sought about any penalty clauses applying if the loan is repaid early.
- The formal written offer from the FHSA or Health Board, including the interim cost rent calculation, should allow the practice to evaluate the financial soundness of the proposed project.
- A practice should not enter into any substantial financial commitments, such as the purchase of land or property, before a formal written offer of cost rent reimbursement has been made.
- A building contract should not be signed until the necessary tenure on the property has been secured and suitable finance has been arranged.
- When premises which are to be rented by the doctors are being developed under the Cost Rent Scheme, the doctors should not enter into a lease before work on the project commences without taking legal advice from the practice solicitor.
- Consideration should be given to taking out insurance against contingencies such as the builder going into liquidation.
- Advice should be sought from the practice accountant about whether registration for VAT under the self-supply regulations is required.
- A separate bank account should be opened, from which all payments relating to the project should be made.
- Application should be made for monthly payments of cost rent or notional rent.

Other issues

- As the project nears completion, the practice should make plans for commissioning the premises.
- Professional advice should be taken before a decision to move from cost rent to notional rent is made.

The above checklist is far from comprehensive. Any practice which finds its present premises inadequate should study this book and the Statement of Fees and Allowances, and should seek advice from the FHSA or Health Board as well as appropriate professional advice. Such careful planning should result in premises of good design which will produce operational and economic benefits for the practice. The doctors and staff will work in more congenial surroundings, which will help to promote better teamwork, improved patient care and a wider range of services to patients.

Index